Growing Up with SCIENCE®

Third Edition

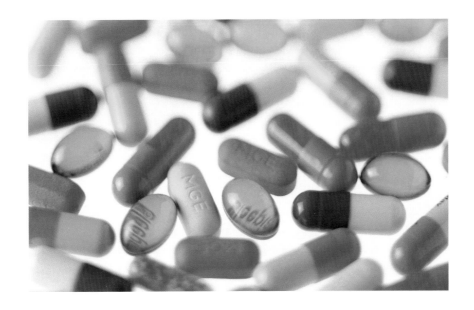

4

Crane–Electricity

 **Marshall Cavendish**
Reference
New York

Marshall Cavendish
99 White Plains Road
Tarrytown, NY 10591

www.marshallcavendish.us

© 2006 Marshall Cavendish Corporation
© 1987, 1990 Marshall Cavendish Limited

GROWING UP WITH SCIENCE is a registered trademark
of Marshall Cavendish Corporation

Library of Congress Cataloging-in-Publication Data

Growing up with science.— 3rd ed.
        p.   cm.
    Includes index.
    Contents: v. 1. Abrasive-Astronomy — v. 2. Atmosphere-Cable television —
v. 3. Cable travel-Cotton — v. 4. Crane-Electricity — v. 5 Electric motor-
Friction — v. 6. Fuel cell-Immune system — v. 7. Induction-Magnetism —
v. 8. Mapmaking-Mining and quarrying — v. 9. Missile and torpedo-Oil
exploration and refining — v. 10. Optics-Plant kingdom — v. 11. Plasma
physics-Radiotherapy — v. 12. Railroad system-Seismology — v. 13.
Semiconductor-Sports — v. 14. Spring-Thermography — v. 15. Thermometer-
Virus, biological — v. 16. Virus, computer-Zoology — v. 17. Index.
ISBN 0-7614-7505-2 (set)
ISBN 0-7614-7509-5 (vol. 4)
1. Science—Encyclopedias.

Q121.G764 2006
503—dc22

2004049962
09 08 07 06 05 6 5 4 3 2 1

Printed in China

CONSULTANT

Donald R. Franceschetti, Ph.D.

Dunavant Professor at the University of Memphis

Donald R. Franceschetti is a member of the American
Chemical Society, the American Physical Society, the
Cognitive Science Society, the History of Science Society,
and the Society for Neuroscience.

CONTRIBUTORS TO VOLUME 4

Chris Cooper   Tom Jackson

Marshall Cavendish

Editor: Peter Mavrikis

Editorial Director: Paul Bernabeo

Production Manager: Alan Tsai

The Brown Reference Group

Editors: Leon Gray and Simon Hall

Designer: Sarah Williams

Picture Researcher: Helen Simm

Indexer: Kay Ollerenshaw

Illustrators: Darren Awuah and Mark Walker

Managing Editor: Bridget Giles

Art Director: Dave Goodman

CONTENTS

KEY TO COLOR CODING OF ARTICLES

 EARTH, SPACE, AND ENVIRONMENTAL SCIENCES   PHYSICS AND CHEMISTRY

LIFE SCIENCES AND MEDICINE   TECHNOLOGY

MATHEMATICS   PEOPLE

Crane

Cranes lift and carry heavy loads for all sorts of industries. They shift material around docks and building sites and keep the flow of work moving inside foundries and other factories. Cranes are relatively simple machines, but they play a major role in the shipping and construction industries.

It is hard to understand how ancient people built their huge stone temples and tombs without any kind of lifting device to help them. Yet the earliest record of a crane dates from the first century BCE, so these machines were probably invented by the ancient Greeks or Roman engineers.

Cranes in history

According to descriptions of early cranes, one type was made of a single pole, the bottom of which was sunk deep into the ground. The crane was held upright by two back stays (strong rope supports). A pulley, which held the hauling ropes, was fixed to the top. The pulley was usually operated by a windlass (a winding device) attached near the base of the pole on one side.

Another early crane was made of two beams tied together at the top and separated into two legs at the bottom. Wooden cross beams held these legs apart, and the windlass was set between them. Two or more people stood inside a cagelike treadmill and worked the crane by walking the treadmill.

The chief problems with early cranes were that they could not swing very far to the right or left, the reach was only as long as the length of the beam used, and the machine was hard to move. These problems were solved in the Middle Ages.

▶ *Gantry cranes are often used at ports. These huge cranes are a type of bridge crane and can lift heavy loads. In this picture, gantry cranes are offloading cargo containers from a container ship.*

The main pole, which by then had been given a jutting arm called a jib at the top end, was supported by a strong wooden frame built around it. This frame held the windlass or treadmill, so that the pole could be turned from inside. The raised load could then be swung as far to the left or right as the jib could go. Moreover, the frame could be hung on the wall as it was being built by setting it into grooves at the sides. The cranes thus no longer had to remain in one place on the ground.

MODERN CRANES

Lifting and moving heavy loads is so much a part of modern industry that many different types of cranes have been designed to cope with a wide variety of uses. The three main kinds of cranes are the bridge crane, jib crane, and tower crane.

Bridge cranes

As their name suggests, bridge cranes straddle the load to be lifted. The winch (known as the trolley), from which the lifting hook hangs, travels back and forth across the overhead bridge. Inside factories, such as foundries and steel mills, the bridge runs up and down on elevated frameworks, called gantries, built against the walls. The crane can then pick up

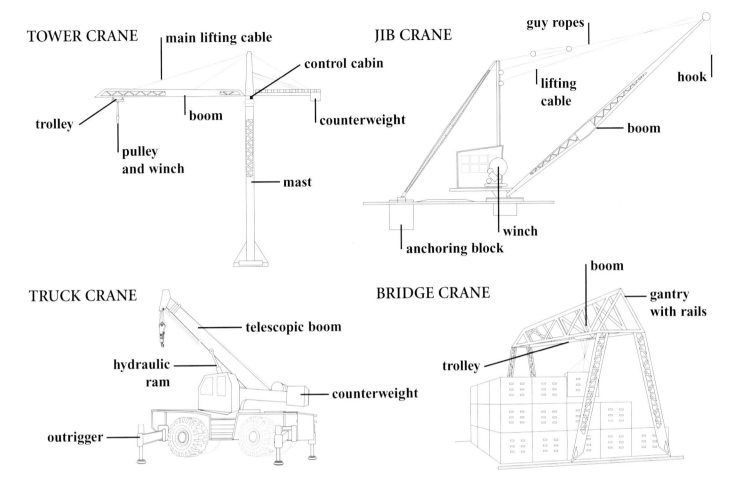

TOWER CRANE
main lifting cable
control cabin
trolley
boom
counterweight
pulley
and winch
mast

JIB CRANE
guy ropes
lifting
cable
hook
boom
winch
anchoring block

TRUCK CRANE
telescopic boom
hydraulic ram
counterweight
outrigger

BRIDGE CRANE
boom
gantry
with rails
trolley

▲ *Bridge, jib, and tower cranes are the most common crane types. Truck cranes are a type of jib crane and are useful because of their mobility.*

and put down a load anywhere in the workplace without taking up any floor space itself. In bridge cranes outside, the bridge is carried on legs that run up and down on rails or wheels, giving the crane maneuverability. Bridge cranes often straddle railroads and roadways and have a crossbeam fitted instead of a hook, allowing the cranes to handle the containers that fit on trucks and railroad flat cars.

Jib cranes

Jib cranes have a jib, which is the projecting arm of the crane. These jib cranes are usually built in a lattice construction that gives strength while saving weight. On many jib cranes, the jib can be raised or lowered and swung around. The load can therefore be picked up from anywhere within the working area. Most of the lifting is done, however, by the

cable that holds the hook, rather than the jib controls. Boom cranes are another variety of jib crane specially built so that they can be driven to wherever a lifting job has to be done. The boom is telescopic, usually consisting of rectangular steel sections. To give extra stability, the carrying truck has extending rams that hold the crane steady when it is lifting a load.

Tower cranes

Tower cranes (also called cantilever cranes) are a special form of jib crane in which the jib runs out horizontally, supported by a tower. Tower cranes virtually build themselves by raising the tower sections into place with a jacking system. Jib cranes need some kind of counterweight, or support system, to keep them from tipping over under load.

See also: BUILDING TECHNIQUES • EARTHMOVER

Crick, Francis, and James Watson

Francis Crick and James Watson solved the puzzle of the genetic code. Their discovery of the structure of deoxyribonucleic acid (DNA) in 1953 made possible a better understanding of heredity and genetic diseases. In recognition of their achievement, Crick and Watson were awarded the Nobel Prize for physiology or medicine in 1962.

English scientist Francis Crick (1916–2004) originally trained as a physicist and worked on magnetic mines and radar during World War II (1939–1945). On his return to research, Crick decided to study biology. In 1949, he joined the Strangeways Research Laboratory at Cambridge University, Britain. Shortly after, Crick moved to the Medical Research Council's Laboratory Molecular Biology Unit at the Cavendish Laboratory in Cambridge. There, Crick studied large organic molecules using X-ray techniques.

Crick meets Watson

In 1951, Crick met U.S. biologist James D. Watson (1928–), who had enrolled at the University of Chicago at the age of 15 and graduated at 19. Watson did his postgraduate research on viruses at the University of Indiana and obtained his doctorate in 1951. He continued his work on viruses at Copenhagen University, Denmark, but moved to the Cavendish Laboratory to study the structure of DNA—the nucleic acid that contains the genetic instructions controlling inheritance.

◀ This photo of Francis Crick (left) and James Watson (right) was taken in 1993. Crick was a student at the Cavendish Laboratory, Cambridge, when he first met Watson in 1951. Both men were interested in DNA, and they agreed to work together to work out the structure of the molecule.

The fact that genes are composed of DNA was already established, and a significant amount of work had been done by many scientists to determine the characteristics and properties of DNA. Using this existing research, Crick and Watson developed a model for the structure of the DNA molecule. Their model consisted of a double helix made up of parallel strands of nucleotides. Nucleotides are formed from a sugar molecule, a molecule of phosphoric acid (H_3PO_4), and a sequence of four bases containing nitrogen. Two of the bases are complementary, so they pair up and join the two nucleotide strands. This makes the whole arrangement coil up like a corkscrew. Crick and Watson built a series of molecular models, gradually modifying them to account for all the known features of DNA.

The final model also provided a mechanism for the duplication of DNA. Crick and Watson proposed that the two strands gradually uncoiled, with two new DNA strands building up on the exposed sequence of bases. Details of the proposed structure were published in 1953, and subsequent work by a number of researchers provided the confirmation that it was correct. Crick and Watson shared the 1962 Nobel Prize for physiology or medicine, along with New Zealand–born British physicist Maurice Wilkins (1916–2004), who supplied vital information in the form of X-ray diffraction studies of the DNA structure. The fourth member of the scientific team, Rosalind Franklin (1920–1958), died before the award was made. Her X-ray photographs were instrumental in confirming Crick and Watson's discovery.

Watson returned to the United States in 1953. In 1961, he became professor of biology at Harvard University, where he worked on the genetic code. In 1968, he became director of the Cold Spring Harbor Laboratory in New York. Among the books he wrote and cowrote were *The Double Helix* (1968) and *The DNA Story* (1981). Crick continued his research at Cambridge University, eventually determining the way in which the DNA molecule stores information. He also established the structure of the basic coding unit.

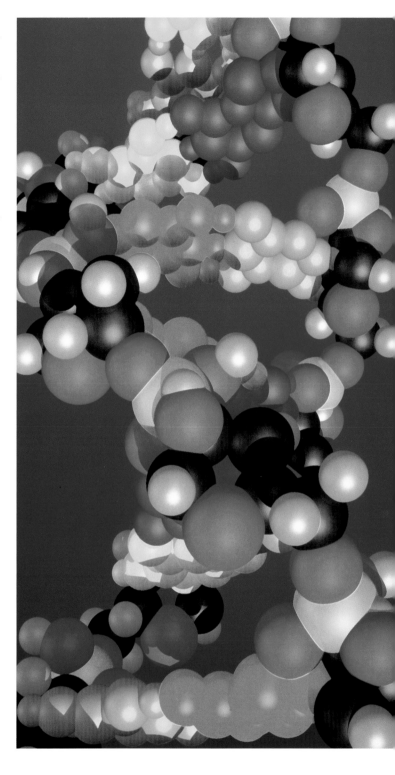

▲ *This is a computer model of the DNA molecule. DNA consists of parallel strands, called nucleotides, twisted like a corkscrew. Each nucleotide is made up of sugar molecules connected by phosphate groups. The strands are linked by molecules called bases.*

See also: DNA • MOLECULAR BIOLOGY

Cryogenics

There is a temperature that is so cold that substances cannot be cooled any further. This temperature is called absolute zero. When materials are cooled to near absolute zero, strange things happen to them. The production of supercold temperatures and the study of substances at these temperatures is called cryogenics.

The body of a hairy mammoth was found in Siberia in the 1990s. Even though this huge animal had been dead for thousands of years—mammoths have long been extinct—the ice had preserved the body. The extreme cold had stopped most of the chemical reactions that would normally have decomposed the carcass.

States of matter

All materials exist in any of the three main states of matter—solid, liquid, or gas. (At very high temperatures, such as in stars, there is a fourth state of matter called plasma.) The state depends upon the temperature of the material and the pressure under which it is placed. Water can be found in all three states of matter: ice in the freezer, liquid water from the faucet, and steam from a boiling kettle.

When a material is heated, the atoms from which it is made gain energy. In the solid state, the atoms vibrate about averaged fixed positions. When they have gained enough energy to leave their positions, the solid melts to a liquid. As the temperature of the liquid increases, the atoms break free from one another. The liquid then boils and evaporates as a gas.

▼ *A technician stores human sperm cells in a cryogenic refrigerator. The technique, called cryopreservation, is also used to store human embryos.*

At normal room temperature, many kinds of foods begin to decompose. Liquid nitrogen coolers and freezers are used to preserve the food once it leaves the factory in which it is manufactured.

Because atoms slow down at low temperatures, cryogenics makes it easier for scientists to study the chemical reactions of many materials.

Liquid air and superfluids

Oxygen and nitrogen in the air are normally found as gases and cannot be seen. If these gases are made supercold, however, they become liquids—in the same way that steam condenses to water. Oxygen becomes a liquid at 90K (−297°F or −183°C), nitrogen at 77K (−320°F or −196°C), and helium at 4K (−452°F or −269°C).

Liquid helium is colorless and has a density about one eighth that of water. A pressure about 25 times that of the atmosphere is needed to turn liquid helium into a solid. Liquid helium is the only substance that does not become solid as absolute zero is approached. It turns into a superfluid below 2.2K (−455°F or −271°C) and stops boiling—the surface of the liquid helium becomes calm. Superfluid helium is called helium II and has zero viscosity, or perfect runniness.

Practical uses

There are many practical uses of supercold materials. Rocket motors that lift astronauts into space use a mixture of liquid hydrogen and oxygen as fuel. In oil exploration, liquid nitrogen is used to cool the drill as it bores through the rock. Liquid nitrogen is also used to keep foods cool in transit.

Biological research uses supercold temperatures to inspect and store some of the cells that make up the human body. The use of liquid nitrogen in medical treatment is also important. Cryosurgery uses cold to kill cells in the body or to stop pain while an operation is performed. Liquid nitrogen is used to destroy unwanted growths such as tumors.

Absolute zero

When a solid is cooled, the vibrations of the atoms get smaller. If the cooling continues, then a temperature will be reached at which the vibrations have the absolute minimum energy required by the laws of physics, and no more cooling is possible. This lowest temperature is called absolute zero. Absolute zero was predicted by scientists even before it was possible to measure it. Modern laboratories have now cooled materials to a few millionths of a degree above absolute zero.

The scientific scale of temperature is the absolute scale. It is measured in degrees Kelvin, named for Scottish scientist Lord Kelvin (William Thomson; 1824–1907). On the Kelvin scale, absolute zero is called 0K, which is the same as −459.67°F (−273.15°C). The freezing point of water is 273.15K (32°F or 0°C), and the boiling point of water is 373.15K (212°F or 100°C).

Properties at low temperatures

When substances are cooled to near absolute zero, their properties often become very different. The movement of atoms almost stops, and most substances shrink in size. Many substances, such as iron and plastic, become very brittle and shatter easily. Electrical properties change, and some pure metals become superconducting, offering no resistance to electrical current.

See also: SUPERCONDUCTIVITY • SURGERY

Crystal

Crystals grow to form nonliving substances such as glittering diamonds, common salt, and sugar. Crystals come in all sorts of shapes and sizes, and many are valuable or useful substances. Many natural and artificial materials are now available in crystalline form.

The word *crystal* comes from the Greek *krystallos,* meaning "clear ice," and this is where the expression "crystal clear" comes from. Crystals grow into geometric shapes that show from their outside surfaces how the atoms are arranged inside the crystal. The bonds between the atoms control the crystal's color and other physical properties.

The atoms in a crystal are much too small to be seen with the naked eye. In a process called X-ray crystallography, an X-ray is passed through a crystal to reveal the crystal's structure. The pattern of the atoms is shown by the way the X-rays come out on the other side. A similar process, called electron microscopy, uses a beam of electrons to reveal the pattern of atoms within a crystalline substance. Both processes have shown that even dustlike crystalline substances, such as fine salt used in a shaker, have a regular crystal structure.

Some crystals are easily visible in nature and can make impressive formations, such as the outcrops of quartz or fluoride crystals found in caves or salt forming on rocks where seawater has evaporated. Crystals are often sought after for their value, as is the case with jewels such as rubies, emeralds, and the hardest crystalline substance of all—diamond. However, making artificial crystals that show the characteristic shape of that substance can be very

▶ *Salt crystals are clearly visible in the foreground of this salt pan in Spain. As seawater evaporates, the solution that remains becomes increasingly salty. Eventually, all that remains is a crust of salt.*

difficult. The regular array of atoms within the crystal has to stretch over numerous repetitions without imperfections.

Crystal structures

Diamond is one of the simplest substances. It contains only carbon atoms, the same element that makes up coal and soot. In diamond, the carbon atoms are arranged in regular patterns, with each atom the same distance from four adjacent atoms. The many facets on a diamond that is set into a ring are not the naturally occurring crystal faces but are artificially cut to provide the maximum sparkle.

Other substances have different types of internal structure. Some, such as graphite (another form of carbon), break along cleavage planes to form flat faces. They break this way because the internal bonds holding the carbon atoms together are more stretched out and, therefore, weaker in some directions. Other materials, such as some plastics, metals, stone, cement, and even hair and bone, have forms of internal crystalline structure.

There are a limited number of ways in which atoms can group to form crystals. In fact, there are 14 kinds of elementary groupings of atoms, called

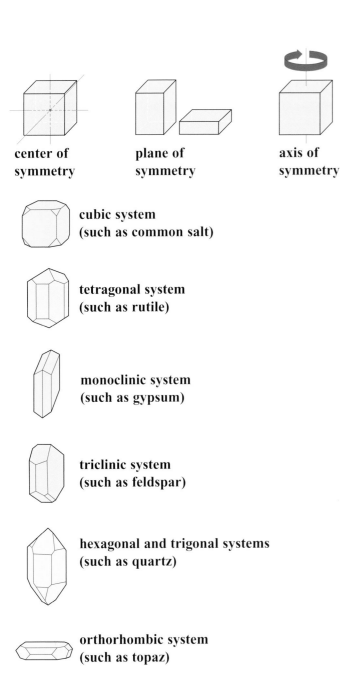

center of symmetry

plane of symmetry

axis of symmetry

cubic system
(such as common salt)

tetragonal system
(such as rutile)

monoclinic system
(such as gypsum)

triclinic system
(such as feldspar)

hexagonal and trigonal systems
(such as quartz)

orthorhombic system
(such as topaz)

▲ *These are some of the most common kinds of crystal structure. The different crystal systems are classified by their symmetry.*

Bravais unit cells. They form the building blocks that, when repeated in certain arrangements, give crystals their characteristic shapes.

Crystal symmetry

The different shapes of unit cells can repeat their patterns in such a way as to produce different kinds of symmetry in the internal crystal structure. In perfect crystals, this will affect the external shape.

Imagine a cube made of modeling clay with a rod placed through from the center of one face to the center of the face opposite. Look straight at one of the other faces and twist the rod a quarter turn. A second face will move around into exactly the same position as the first and so on with further quarter turns. This is called an axis of four-fold symmetry. Stick the rod diagonally through from one corner of the cube to the opposite corner, and this gives an axis of three-fold symmetry. Twisting the rod a third of a turn brings the faces into the same positions.

Altogether there are 32 different classes of crystal symmetry, which give rise to all the different possible shapes, defined by the angles between crystal faces. Although perfect crystals of a particular substance always show the same angles between various faces (angles that are dictated by the shape of the unit cell building blocks), it is the internal structure that shows the regular repeating pattern. The external shape of the crystal may be damaged, but the internal structure is always the same.

Crystallography

Using X-ray crystallography, scientists can discover the pattern of the atoms and molecules within it. The regular arrangement of atoms in a crystal scatters a beam of X-rays into a distinctive pattern. This happens by the process of diffraction. X-ray crystallography works in the same way as light reflecting off a compact disc. The fine pattern of grooves on a compact disc splits up the reflection of a point of light into a line. The reflections from a compact disc look like lines spreading out from the center. Grooves appear as circles around the center of the compact disc, even though the grooves are too small to be seen. In the case of crystallography, the X-ray beam passes through the crystal. The pattern of scattered beams can be analyzed to figure out the size and pattern of the atoms and molecules inside.

Improved methods

X-ray crystallography is a fast and reliable way of looking at crystal structure. Very intense X-rays can now be created by machines called synchrotrons. In a synchrotron, a beam of electrons is made to travel in a huge circle, about the size of a sports stadium. The X-rays produced make it possible to study tiny crystals or large molecules. Cooling the sample down almost to absolute zero—0K (−459.67°F or −273.15°C)—makes the patterns more precise.

Growing crystals

Crystals grow by the addition of new material onto an existing crystal. The atoms fit into a position that extends the regularly repeating pattern. Crystal growth can start with a perfect crystal, just a few atoms across, that have come together by chance, or at a scratch on the surface of a container. More atoms are deposited out of a solution of the substance or from the molten substance. These atoms then add to the solid crystal.

Crystals occur naturally because upheavals in Earth's crust (such as volcanoes) have produced the conditions of heat and pressure under which molten or dissolved material can crystallize slowly.

▼ *The synchrotron at Lawrence Berkeley Laboratory, California, is one of the most advanced in the world. X-rays are fired through the crystals of proteins to provide information about their internal structure.*

Crystals are also grown commercially using processes such as crystal pulling, where a perfect seed crystal is dipped into a molten bath of substance and slowly withdrawn. High-grade crystals are vital to industries such as those producing the microchips at the heart of modern computers. One of the hopes associated with space experiments is that crystal growth under zero-gravity conditions will form even better crystals.

Synthetic crystals

The term *synthetic crystals* refers to a few hundred different crystals that are valuable as gemstones, in industry, or both. It does not include those crystals made in large commercial quantities, such as sugar, common salt, and detergents. Many gemstones, such as diamonds, emeralds, rubies, and sapphires, can be made artificially. However, synthetic gemstones are not as valuable as natural ones.

Diamond is the hardest known substance in the world, and it proved to be the most difficult crystal to synthesize. Many people claim to be the first to make synthetic diamond. However, it is generally accepted that the first synthesis of diamond was

Modern manufacturing processes

Many gemstones and industrial-quality crystals are produced by the Czochralski technique. This process is named for Polish scientist Jan Czochralski (1885–1953), who perfected the technique of crystal growth in 1917. Czochralski dipped a small seed of the crystal into the molten form of the same crystal. As the seed was slowly withdrawn, the molten mixture around it cooled, and a long crystal formed. Impurities remain in the melt, so that the cooled crystal is purer than the original solution. The crystal can be purified further by zone refining. In this process, a small part of the crystal is melted. The heat is moved down the crystal, taking the impurities with it. The impurities come together at one end of the crystal, which is then discarded.

Crystals can also be grown from vapor, from low-temperature solutions, high-temperature solutions, from a solid, and by hydrothermal methods.

Uses of synthetic crystals

Many synthetic crystals are used in industry as abrasives for cutting, cleaning, or polishing. The first synthetic abrasive to be produced commercially was silicon carbide in 1891. One of the most recent synthetic abrasives is cubic boron nitride, which does not occur in nature. Cubic boron nitride and diamond have a very similar structure. Once scientists synthesized diamond, they realized they could also produce cubic boron nitride.

Another type of synthetic crystal, made of plastic, has been developed for use in fiber-optic telephone systems. Fiber-optic systems send telephone calls through hair-thin strands of glass as flashes of laser light. However, devices called switchers, which sort out the flashes of the various conversations, could not work as fast as the laser could. As a result, the number of calls that could be handled was limited. Scientists have now made ultrafast switchers for the fiber-optic systems from these crystals, and the new systems can handle one thousand times more calls.

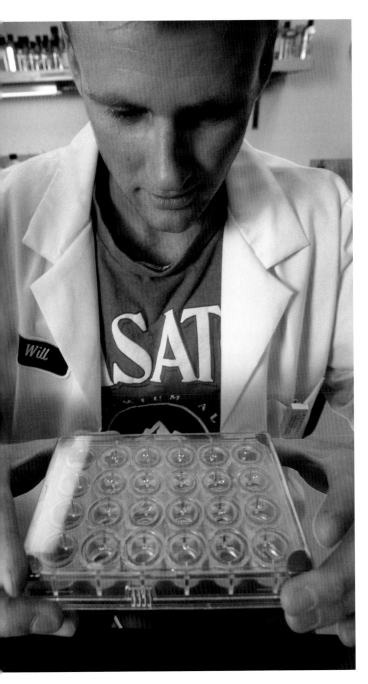

▲ *This biologist is conducting laboratory research on a protein crystal. It is easier for the biologist to study the protein if it is in the form of a crystal.*

accomplished in 1955 at the General Electric plant in Schenectady, New York. The process used produced diamonds only for industrial use. Diamonds of gemstone quality can be made artificially, but the process is too expensive to be done commercially. However, there is a great demand for industrial diamonds, which are used as abrasives in tools.

See also: CARBON • DIAMOND • X-RAY

Curie, Marie and Pierre

The work of Marie and Pierre Curie was essential to the development of modern chemistry and physics. Their studies of radioactivity revealed much about the atom, and they discovered the radioactive elements polonium and radium. In recognition of their important contribution to science, the element curium, discovered in 1944, was named for them.

Pierre Curie was born in Paris, France, on May 15, 1859. As a youth, Pierre was educated at home by his father, who was a physician, and then attended the Sorbonne University, Paris. After passing his final examinations, Pierre took a job in the university laboratories as a demonstrator. He also conducted his own research with his brother Jacques. An experiment in 1880 led to the discovery that pressure on some crystals produces electricity. This phenomenon is called piezoelectricity, and it is used in many modern devices. Pierre also made important discoveries about magnetism and was awarded his doctorate in 1895. That same year, he married a fellow student named Marie (originally Maria) Sklodowska.

▼ *Marie (right) and Pierre Curie (center) made their discoveries under conditions of great hardship. Their laboratories were barely adequate, and they had to do other work to earn their livelihood.*

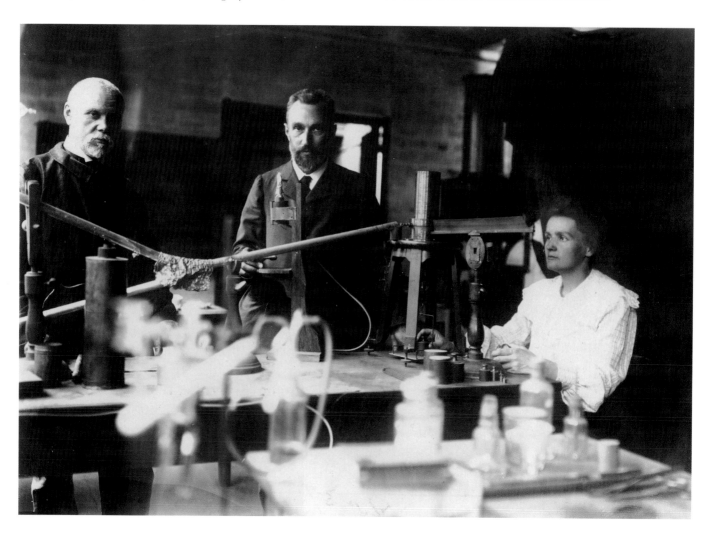

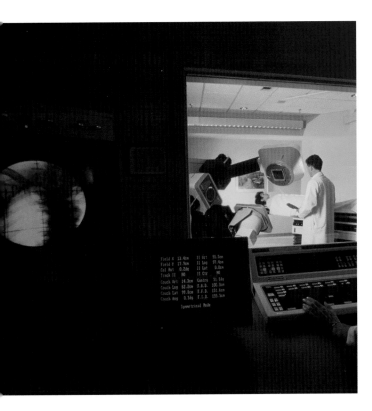

▲ *The current use of radiation in medical imaging and in the treatment of various cancers owes much to the pioneering work of Marie Curie.*

Maria Sklodowska was born in Warsaw, Poland, on November 7, 1867. Although she did very well at school, Marie started work at 16 because her father had lost all his money. In 1891, she went to Paris to study at the Sorbonne. She was very poor and had to live in a tiny room with little to eat except bread and butter. On one occasion, Marie fainted from hunger during a lecture. Despite this hardship, she did brilliantly well at the Sorbonne.

Marie's marriage to Pierre in 1895 formed a partnership that was to become world famous. Two years later, they had a daughter and named her Irène.

Investigations of radioactivity

In 1895, French physicist Antoine Henri Becquerel (1852–1908) discovered strange rays coming from uranium. Marie did her own research and found that thorium gave off similar rays. She called this property radioactivity. Further studies revealed that an ore called pitchblende was more radioactive than either uranium or thorium. Marie realized that it must contain a stronger radioactive substance. At this point, Pierre gave up his own research, and together they tried to isolate the new substance. In 1898, they announced that they had discovered not one new chemical element, but two. Marie called one of them polonium, after her native country, and the other radium. Pierre also made important studies of the radiation emitted by these elements.

In 1903, Marie and Pierre Curie and Becquerel received the Nobel Prize for physics for their work on radioactivity. Marie became the first woman ever to win a Nobel Prize and was immediately awarded a doctorate. In the following year, Pierre became a professor at the Sorbonne and their second daughter, Eve, was born. The Curies were becoming world famous when, in 1906, Pierre was run over by a wagon and tragically killed.

Marie took over Pierre's post as professor at the Sorbonne, becoming the first woman to teach there. She continued her attempts to obtain pure samples of the new elements so that she could study them further. In 1910, after ten years of hard work involving tons of pitchblende, she held pure radium in her hands. In 1911, Marie received the Noble Prize for chemistry for this work and for the discovery of new elements.

A mother and daughter team

During World War I (1914–1918), Marie worked with her daughter Irène on the use of X-rays in medicine. Irène went on to form another brilliant scientific partnership with her own husband, Frédéric Joliot. In 1935, Irène and Frédéric Joliot-Curie won their own Nobel Prize for chemistry.

During the 1920s, Marie worked mainly on chemistry and the medical uses of radioactivity. Although the dangers of radiation were known by this time, she took few precautions when handling radioactive substances. In 1934, she died of leukemia brought on by radiation. Soon after her death, Marie's book *Radioactivité* was published, summarizing much of her work.

See also: RADIOACTIVITY

399

Cyclone

A cyclone is a severe tropical storm. Cyclones are known as hurricanes in the United States and the Caribbean, typhoons in the China Sea, and willy-willies in Australia. Cyclones are areas of low air pressure and fast winds, which spin around a central eye. When cyclones pass over land, they cause widespread damage.

Cyclones may be between 100 and 300 miles (160 and 480 kilometers) across. They develop over the oceans between latitudes 5 and 25 degrees north, and 5 and 25 degrees south. They never seem to form in the region close to the equator between 5 degrees north and 5 degrees south.

For a cyclone to form, the sea surface must have a temperature of at least 81°F (27°C). In such warm areas, the lower layers of air are heated and they rise upward, creating a large low-pressure air system. This rising air is moist, because it contains much evaporated water in the form of invisible water vapor from the sea.

The supply of heat and moisture is essential in the formation of cyclones. Cyclones soon die out if they drift over cooler seas. They also die out quickly when they move over dry land because they are deprived of their water supply, which is essential for their continued existence.

Except at the center (called the eye), the air in a cyclone rises upward in a series of spirals. Air flows into the cyclone at ground level to replace the rising air. This air is also heated and it, too, rises. Because of the rotation (spin) of Earth, incoming air does not flow directly toward the center. Instead it is deflected to form a rotating air system. In the Northern Hemisphere, the winds are deflected in a clockwise direction in any low-pressure air system. South of the equator, the air is deflected in a counterlockwise direction.

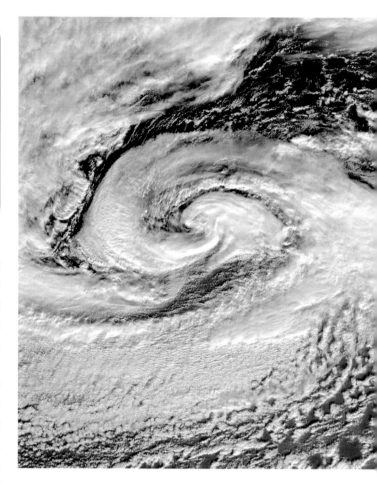

▲ *A NASA spacecraft captured this image of a cyclone just south of Kamchatka Peninsula and the Aleutian Islands in the northwestern Pacific in 2002.*

As the air rises, it cools, and water vapor condenses to form water droplets. Billions of these droplets form dense cumulus and cumulonimbus (thunderstorm) clouds. Heat is produced when water vapor condenses, and this heat intensifies the processes at work. Thunder, lightning, and heavy rain are features of cyclones, with the heaviest rain occurring just outside the ring of strongest winds around the central eye. In 1954, for example, Hurricane Alice brought 27 inches (68.5 centimeters) of rain to much of southwest Texas.

The clouds start to form around the center of the cyclone, but they soon spiral outward as nimbostratus, cumulostratus, and cirrus clouds form. The

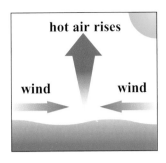

▲ *Cyclones occur when areas of low pressure form over warm tropical seas. Low pressure is created when air above the sea heats up and rises. Winds rush into the low pressure zone.*

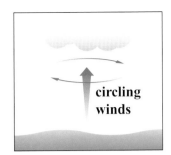

▲ *As the rising air and winds meet, they circle around due to Earth's rotation. Winds circle clockwise in the Northern Hemisphere and counterclockwise in the Southern Hemisphere.*

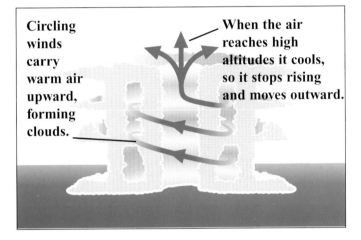

Circling winds carry warm air upward, forming clouds.

When the air reaches high altitudes it cools, so it stops rising and moves outward.

▲ *The cyclone moves over the ocean and continues to suck up warm, moist air. It loses its power if it passes over cool water or land. Cyclones can measure up to 300 miles (480 kilometers) across, with winds of 200 miles (320 kilometers) per hour. However, the center, or eye, of the cyclone is calm.*

eye of a cyclone is a region of light winds where air subsides. By the time this air reaches the oceans, it is very warm. This helps maintain the low air pressures at the center of the storm. The energy of the cyclone is derived mainly from the release of heat in the updraft around the eye.

In the path of a cyclone

The first sign of an approaching cyclone is often a change in wind direction as the spiraling winds of the cyclone replace the normal prevailing winds.

High clouds, called cirrus clouds, start to spread, and gradually the clouds become lower and thicker. Soon the air pressure drops and wind speeds increase. Rain squalls then occur, and the sea along coasts becomes increasingly choppy.

As the storm intensifies, wind speeds rise to over 100 miles (160 kilometers) per hour, reaching perhaps 150 to 200 miles (240 to 320 kilometers) per hour when the storm reaches its height. High waves batter the shore, often causing floods. The high winds uproot trees, tear the roofs off houses, and sweep away automobiles and trains.

Soon after the storm has reached its peak, the sky lightens and the rain stops. The eye has arrived. The eye can be up to 30 miles (48 kilometers) across, and it may take up to four hours for it to pass overhead. During this period, the weather is warm and the sky is almost clear of clouds.

The storm then starts again. The sky is once more filled with heavy clouds, rain lashes down, and winds blow in the opposite direction from those that preceded the eye. This is because cyclones are circular storms. Eventually, wind speeds decrease and the sky brightens, although the rain may continue for some time.

Monitoring cyclones

The development of high-altitude research airplanes and weather satellites has helped meteorologists to better understand the formation of cyclones. Much information is collected by radar equipment and other instruments. Satellite photographs show clearly the swirling pattern of clouds in cyclones. From space, the eye is usually identifiable at what looks like the center of a whirlpool. By tracking the movements of the eye, the speed at which the cyclone is moving and the direction it is taking can be constantly checked. Warnings can then be issued to the public. In the United States, 24-hour forecasts of the path of a cyclone over land can be given.

See also: CLOUD • RAIN AND RAINFALL • TORNADO • WIND

Dalton, John

John Dalton was an English scientist. Hailed as the "father of meteorology," he was an avid weather watcher and an accomplished chemist. He proposed the atomic theory of matter, which is one of the basic theories of science.

Dalton was born in a village called Eaglesfield in Cumbria, England, on September 5 or 6, 1766. The son of a Quaker weaver, Dalton remained a Quaker throughout his life. Dalton started teaching at the age of 12, and in 1780 he moved to a school in Kendal where he taught for the next 12 years.

Dalton lived in England's mountainous Lake District, so he was in an ideal place to observe weather events. He developed a keen interest in meteorology—the study of the weather and the atmosphere. In 1787, Dalton started to record the weather in a diary. By the time he died on July 27, 1844, the diary contained more than 200,000 entries. Dalton also noted other phenomena, such as auroras (multicolored flashing lights in the night sky). From his detailed observations he made many important meteorological discoveries. Despite

▲ *This portrait of John Dalton was painted in 1834. Dalton was one of England's greatest scientists, but he was unaffected by fame and lived a simple life.*

contemporary opinion, he became convinced that the atmosphere was a physical mixture of elements (approximately 80 percent nitrogen and 20 percent oxygen) rather than being a specific compound of elements. Dalton published a book entitled *Meteorological Observations and Essays* in 1793. Although the book did not have a huge impact a the time, it contained many original ideas and came to mark the transition of meteorology from a topic of general interest to a serious science. In recognition of his work, Dalton is often called the "father of meteorology."

DID YOU KNOW?

When Dalton moved to Manchester in 1793, he joined the Manchester Literary and Philosophical Society. Later, he became secretary of the society, and his first contribution was a paper on the defect that he had discovered in his own and his brother's vision. The paper was the first scientific account of color blindness, which for some time after was called Daltonism. In 1817, Dalton became president of the society—an honorary office that he held until his death in 1844.

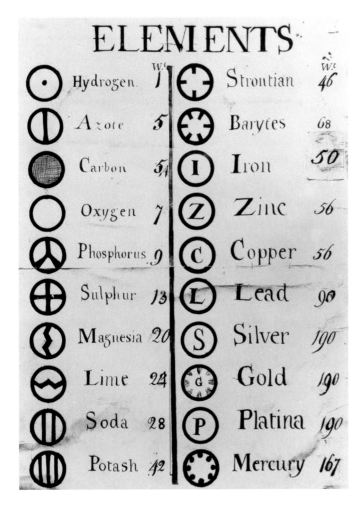

ELEMENTS

Hydrogen	1	Strontian	46
Azote	5	Barytes	68
Carbon	54	Iron	50
Oxygen	7	Zinc	56
Phosphorus	9	Copper	56
Sulphur	13	Lead	90
Magnesia	20	Silver	190
Lime	24	Gold	190
Soda	28	Platina	190
Potash	42	Mercury	167

◄ *This picture shows Dalton's chart of the chemical elements, which was published in 1805. Dalton's original chart includes substances such as soda (sodium carbonate; Na_2CO_3) and potash (potassium carbonate; K_2CO_3), which chemists now know to be compounds—mixtures of different elements.*

Move to Manchester

In 1793, Dalton accepted a post at New College, Manchester, as a teacher of mathematics and philosophy. New College was founded by Presbyterians, who wanted to provide a first-class education to candidates for the ministry. At the time, only members of the Church of England could study at Britain's prestigious Cambridge or Oxford universities. Dalton had no formal experience in chemistry, and he taught from a book called *Elements of Chemistry* (1789) by French chemist Antoine-Laurent Lavoisier (1743–1794). Chemistry clearly interested Dalton. In 1800, he gave up teaching to conduct research in the subject.

Atomic theory

Dalton produced many inspired ideas as a chemist. His early research on gases led to the development of the law of partial pressures, which Dalton published in 1802. Dalton's law states that every gas in a mixture behaves independently, exerting the same pressure it would have if it were the only gas present. In other words, the total pressure of a mixture of gases equals the sum of the pressures of every gas in the mixture.

Dalton's work on the law of partial pressures led him to the conclusion that the atoms (particles of matter) in different elements are not alike. He claimed that atoms of different elements vary in size and mass, and this fact formed the founding principle of his atomic theory of matter. Dalton devised a system of chemical symbols for each element and then attempted to determine the relative masses of each different kind of atom by measuring how various elements, such as carbon, hydrogen, nitrogen, and oxygen, combined with fixed masses of each other. In 1803, Dalton arranged the elements into a table.

Dalton's atomic theory of matter relied on several assumptions:

1) All matter consists of atoms. Atoms are both indivisible and indestructible.

2) All atoms of a given element are identical in mass and properties.

3) Compounds are formed by a combination of two or more different kinds of atoms.

4) A chemical reaction is a rearrangement of atoms.

Dalton was a quiet and modest man. He lived simply, in keeping with his Quaker faith. He died of a stroke just after recording the day's weather in his diary on July 27, 1844. Dalton's last experiment came after his death. He requested that an autopsy determine the cause of his color blindness. The autopsy revealed that the condition was not caused by the eye itself but by some sensory deficiency.

See also: ATOM AND MOLECULE • CHEMISTRY • ELEMENT, CHEMICAL • GAS • METEOROLOGY

Dam

Dams are barriers built across rivers to control and harness the flow of water for specific purposes, including electric power generation, flood control, irrigation, navigation, and water supply. Most modern dams are designed to serve more than one of these purposes.

Since ancient times, people have built dams across rivers to store water for their towns and cities, to irrigate their crops, and to protect themselves from floods. Ruins of almost prehistoric dams exist in the Nile and Tigris Valleys. In Italy, some Roman dams dating back two thousand years are still in use. Modern dams are often designed to perform other jobs, too, and contain electric power generators and locks to allow ships to pass through.

Dams are built from bricks, concrete, earth, or rock. Each dam is built to suit the site on which it is constructed and, if possible, materials that are most readily available.

Building a dam

The first task in building a dam is to divert the river and create a dry building site. For small rivers, a channel is constructed around the site. This is later closed off. For larger rivers this is impractical, so engineers build a coffer dam. A coffer dam is a temporary enclosure of metal or sand and rock formed on one side of the river, allowing the river to flow around it. The coffer dam is pumped dry and the first section of the dam is built. When this section is complete, engineers construct another coffer dam on the other side of the river and build the final part of the dam. Meanwhile, the river flows through outlets in the completed section, and the reservoir (a lake used for water supply) can start to fill behind it.

Embankment dams

Embankment dams are the most common type of dams. They are often cheap and easy to build. They are filled with either earth or rocks and are usually chosen for sites with wide valleys. They can be built on rock or softer soil because they have wide bases that do not put too much pressure on their foundations. The earth or crushed rock is built up

▶ *The Diablo Dam on the upper Skagit River in Washington is an example of an arch dam. The arched shape of the dam adds to its strength and means that it can be made thinner than a traditional embankment or gravity dam. Diablo Dam was completed in 1930 and had turbines installed in 1936 for the generation of hydroelectric power.*

in layers to form a triangle shape across the river. At the same time a watertight core of clay is put in. These dams are then usually strengthened with a covering of bricks, concrete, or stone blocks.

The biggest earth-fill dam in the world is the Tarbela Dam on the Indus River in Pakistan. Completed in 1975, it is 470 feet (143 meters) tall and was built to create a reservoir for irrigation. The amount of material in the dam exceeds the amount used to build the Great Wall of China.

Gravity dams

Gravity dams are so called because the weight of the material used to build the dam holds it in place. They are usually made of bricks, concrete, or stone blocks. Again, the cross section of the dam is a broad-based triangle. Gravity dams are suitable for wide or narrow valleys. Unlike embankment dams, however, they need solid rock foundations because they are narrower and heavier. A good example of a gravity dam is the Grande Dixence Dam in Switzerland. At 935 feet (285 meters) tall, it is one of the world's tallest dams. Built to generate electricity, the dam's generators can produce over 2,000 megawatts (1 megawatt is one million watts)—as much as two nuclear power stations.

Buttress dams

Buttress dams can also be used to close very wide rivers. Like gravity dams, they are built from bricks, concrete, or stone blocks with a watertight covering, and they need solid foundations. They are not as thick, however, because they have a row of buttresses (wide supports) reinforcing the down-stream wall. They are therefore lighter than gravity dams. Buttress dams are not as strong, however, and they are not usually very high.

The Zeya Dam on the Eya River in Siberia is one of the world's largest buttress dams. It is 377 feet (115 meters) tall and contains over 10 million cubic yards (8 million cubic meters) of concrete.

Despite thorough engineering, dams can collapse. In June 1976, this happened to a buttress dam in Idaho. Water began trickling through a weak spot in the Teton Dam. The trickle grew to a

BASIC TYPES OF DAMS

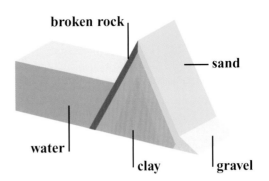

▲ *Embankment dams are the oldest form of dam. The diagram above shows an earth-fill embankment dam.*

▲ *Gravity dams resist the weight of the water by their sheer mass and must have strong foundations.*

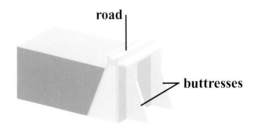

▲ *Buttress dams use strong buttresses to transmit the weight of the water to its foundations.*

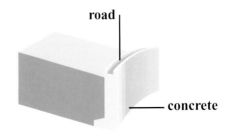

▲ *Arch dams are curved to deflect the weight of the water to its sides and foundations.*

massive flood that swept away the dam and swamped the Snake River valley below, leaving some 30,000 people homeless.

Arch dams

Arch dams are often built across rivers that are not very wide and where there are solid rock foundations. The walls of these dams have a shape that curves similar to an arch upstream against the pressure of water. Arch dams are made from concrete. They are built across narrow canyons between high cliffs. The Hoover Dam on the Colorado River on the border between Arizona and Nevada is a famous example.

The concrete in arch dams does not need to be very thick because of the shape of the dam wall. The great strength of these dams comes from the same principle as arches used to build bridges. As the weight of the water presses on the dam wall, this

weight is transmitted to the walls on either side of the arch. Arch dams therefore need solid rock foundations. This principle was first used by Chryses of Alexandria. It is thought that he built the first arch dam on the Turkish–Syrian border in 560 CE. Chryses claimed that the dam was built "in the form of a crescent so that its arch, which was turned against the stream of water, might be better able to resist the violence."

An impressive arch dam can be found at Sayany on the Yenisei River in Russia. It is 3,500 feet (1,067 meters) long, 794 feet (242 meters) high, and contains about 12 million cubic yards (9 million cubic meters) of concrete. The huge reservoir created behind the dam has a volume of 7.5 cubic miles (31 cubic kilometers). The electricity generated by the water flowing through this vast dam is thought to be 6,400 megawatts.

Cupola dams

The cupola dam is similar to the simple arch dam, but the concrete wall arches out in the vertical face of the dam wall as well as the horizontal face. The double curve of this kind of dam uses the thrust of the water to give it more strength. Cupola dams

▼ The Thames Flood Barrier in London, England, is a semipermanent dam. Huge horizontally rotating steel gates 53 feet (16 meters) high can be closed to prevent surge tides from flooding the city.

▲ *The Three Gorges Dam is being built across the Chang Jiang River in China. When completed, this concrete gravity dam will be the largest dam in the world. The project has been controversial, because the huge human and ecological costs of the project are thought by many to outweigh the perceived benefits.*

need very solid rock foundations. The effect of the great weight of water pressing against the concrete wall is to try to straighten it. The wall is pressed into the rock at either side and into the foundations at the bottom. Cupola dams are the most complicated dams to design. Engineers have to figure out all the forces before the dam is built. A dam breaking can cause widespread flooding and destruction.

Flood barriers

Although a reason for building many dams is for flood control, not all dams need to permanently dam rivers just for this purpose. In some cases, a semipermanent flood barrier is built across a river. These dams have large gates that are usually open to allow the river to flow normally. With the risk of flooding, however, the gates are closed. The largest flood barrier is the 1,716-feet- (597-meter-) wide Thames Flood Barrier in London, England.

Hydroelectric power

The high pressure of water that builds up at the bottom of a large dam is often used to turn the blades of turbines to generate electricity. The water for the turbines is directed down ducts called penstock tubes. As the turbines revolve, they drive shafts connected to electric generators. Electrical power generated in this way is called hydroelectric power. The great benefit of hydroelectric power is that it is "clean," which means it does not harm the environment. Coal- or gas-burning or nuclear power stations all produce harmful emissions.

Effects on ecosystems

Dams bring many benefits, but they also damage the environment in many ways. Large areas of land are flooded when reservoirs fill, and important wildlife habitats are lost. Natural river flooding cycles—threatening to people but important to plants and animals—no longer take place. Dams also hold back sediment that once renewed eroded beaches where rivers finally meet the sea.

See also: BRIDGE • BUILDING TECHNIQUES

Darwin, Charles

English naturalist Charles Darwin proposed the theory of evolution by natural selection. Many people now consider Darwin's theory to be one of the greatest achievements in the history of the biological sciences. However, many of his contemporaries could not reconcile his theory with their own religious beliefs.

Charles Darwin was born in Shrewsbury, England, on February 12, 1809. In 1818, he went to Shrewsbury School, but he was not interested in his studies. When he was 16, his physician father told him "You care for nothing but shooting, dogs, and rat-catching, and you will be a disgrace to yourself and all your family."

Darwin went on to study medicine in Edinburgh, Scotland, but again he did little work. So his father sent him to Cambridge University to study for a career in the church. Darwin had little time for his religious studies. Instead, he preferred to read and talk about natural history with many famous scientists at Cambridge University. One of these was John Henslow (1796–1861), a professor of botany at the university.

In 1831, Henslow was asked to suggest a naturalist to take part in a voyage of HMS *Beagle,* and he suggested Darwin. Henslow must have seen some special quality in Darwin, for there were many better qualified people around. At first, Darwin's father insisted that he stay and complete his studies. But his uncle, Josiah Wedgwood II, realized that it would be a wonderful opportunity for Darwin and persuaded his father to let him go.

In December 1831, Darwin sailed on HMS *Beagle,* which was captained by Robert Fitzroy. The voyage lasted five years, during which time they explored South America and islands in the Pacific Ocean. They also visited Africa and Australia.

▲ *Darwin did not present his theory of natural selection until many years after the voyage of HMS Beagle. He wanted to ensure that he had enough evidence to make an irrefutable case.*

Controversial ideas

When Darwin was alive, most people believed that God had created Earth and all living things (as explained in the Bible's book of Genesis). They did not think that Earth or the animals and plants that live on the planet could change over time. Darwin took with him on his voyage a book entitled *Principles of Geology* by Scottish geologist Charles Lyell (1797–1875). In his book, Lyell suggested that Earth had existed for millions of years and that its surface was always slowly changing. Darwin studied the geology of the lands he visited and became convinced that Lyell was right. He also made many important geological discoveries, including the way in which coral reefs and atolls form.

▲ *This picture shows Darwin's ship HMS Beagle anchored in the Strait of Magellan near Chile. The ship sailed from England in 1831 to explore the coasts of South America, Australia, and Africa. It returned in 1836.*

In Brazil, Darwin found fossils of creatures, such as mastodons, that no longer existed. These fossils intrigued Darwin. Attracted by the spectacular life around him, he started observing and collecting plant and animals specimens. He particularly noted animals on the Galápagos Islands, a few hundred miles from the coast of Ecuador. Many of these islands contained finches and tortoises, but the species differed slightly from one island to the next. For example, he found 14 species of finches, now called Darwin's finches.

When HMS *Beagle* returned to Britain in 1836, Darwin thought about the specimens he had seen on the voyage. He realized that many things that puzzled him could be explained if animals slowly evolved (changed) over time. For example, the many different finches could have evolved from one common ancestor. He suggested that evolution happened through a process called natural selection.

Although convinced that he was correct, Darwin did not publish his theory. He knew that it would outrage people. Instead, he studied the mass of material he had collected on his voyage and accumulated evidence. Then, in 1858, he was very surprised when Welsh naturalist Alfred Russel Wallace (1823–1913) sent him a letter outlining the same theory. Unlike Darwin, however, Wallace had little evidence to back it up. On July 1, 1858, both men read a joint paper to the Linnaean Society in London. In 1859, Darwin published a brief account of his work called *On the Origin of Species*. This book was an immediate best seller.

Darwin went on to write many other books about the animals and plants he had studied on his travels. By the time he died in 1882, his theory of evolution was acclaimed by scientists all over the world. International honors were showered on him, but all he received from the British government was permission to be buried at Westminster Abbey.

See also: EVOLUTION

Dentistry

Dentistry is concerned with the care and maintenance of teeth. It has developed from crude tooth pulling to modern-day techniques using X-rays, local anesthetics, and microsurgery.

The teeth play an important part in people's lives. When people eat, the mouth is used as the first stage of digestion. With it people taste, chew, moisten, and swallow food. When people speak, they use the mouth, teeth, and tongue. Dental problems interfere with all these activities.

Early dentistry

In 4000 BCE, the ancient Egyptians tried all kinds of cures for their tooth problems. The Chinese in 2000 BCE treated dental complaints with herbs and acupuncture. In the fifth century BCE, the ancient Greeks wrote about the operation of pulling teeth. In the first century CE, the Romans carried out extractions, fillings, and made false teeth. When the Roman Empire fell, however, the treatment of tooth problems seems to have been confined for centuries to pulling out the bad teeth.

By the fourteenth century in England, the barber-surgeons were the experts at dentistry. They cut hair, shaved people, bled the sick, and pulled out people's teeth. The red-and-white striped poles outside their shops were often hung with strings of teeth that had been successfully extracted.

It was not until the nineteenth century and the arrival of drugs called anesthetics that real dentistry as we know it began to be practiced.

Anesthetics

Between 1844 and 1846, U.S. dentists Horace Wells (1815–1848) and William T. G. Morton (1819–1868) started to use ether or nitrous oxide (N_2O) to produce anesthesia for dental extractions. Using these drugs, the patient became completely unconscious.

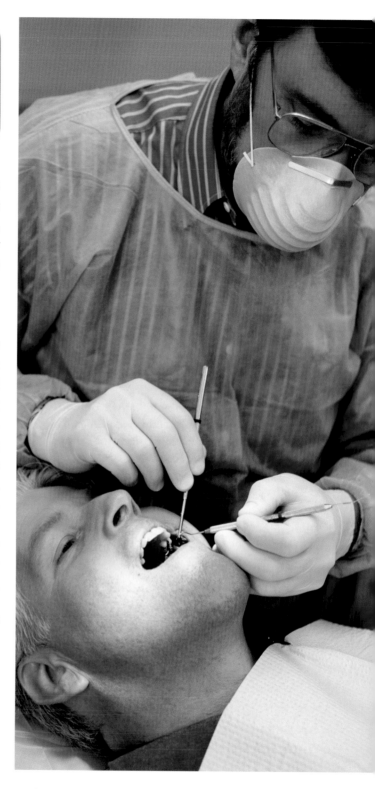

▲ *A patient undergoes a routine dental examination. It is important to have regular dental checkups to ensure that teeth and gums are healthy. The sooner problems are discovered, the easier the treatment.*

Then came local anesthetics. The hypodermic needle had been invented in 1845, but it was not until 1884 that an injection of the drug cocaine was used to make one part of the body insensitive to pain. Anesthetics helped to advance dentistry quickly.

What are teeth made of?

Healthy teeth are held by strong fibers in sockets in the upper and lower jaws. The root is the part of the tooth attached to the jaw. The crown is the visible part of the tooth. Teeth are composed of cementum, dentine, enamel, and pulp. Cementum is a bonelike material that covers the outside of the roots and holds the tooth in the jaw. Dentine makes up most of the rest of the tooth. It is a sensitive substance, fed by liquid that travels through fine tubes inside it. Enamel is the tough white outer coating of the teeth. It is the hardest substance in the entire body. The pulp is the "nerve" of the tooth. It is inside the dentine and goes down into the root of the tooth. While people do not usually think of teeth as living matter, except perhaps for the nerve endings in the pulp canal, there are living cells in the hard matrix of the tooth, nourished by the blood supply to the pulp canal.

Tooth decay

Tooth decay, or dental caries, is the most usual disease to affect the teeth. It is found most often in people who eat foods containing a lot of sugar and other carbohydrates. When food remnants are allowed to collect on the tooth surfaces, they form a scum, or dental plaque. This plaque is full of bacteria, which make a strong acid that attacks the enamel. After a while, the enamel breaks down and other bacteria attack the unprotected dentine. The infection finally reaches the pulp and the result is a toothache. If the infection lasts long enough, the pulp and the nerve endings are killed, giving temporary relief from pain. However, the infection continues down into the root, causing a painful swelling of the jaw. This is called a dental abscess.

Treatment

When teeth are damaged by decay, the infected part can be removed and the hole (cavity) filled. Fillings can be made from silver amalgam, gold, or plastic dental resin colored to look like the tooth. The filling is made soft enough to be packed into the cavity, but it hardens into a substance that is not affected by the chemicals in the mouth's saliva.

DID YOU KNOW?

All rodents have a pair of long curved incisors in both the upper and lower jaws. These teeth grow continuously but are kept to a reasonable length by the rodents' constant gnawing at food.

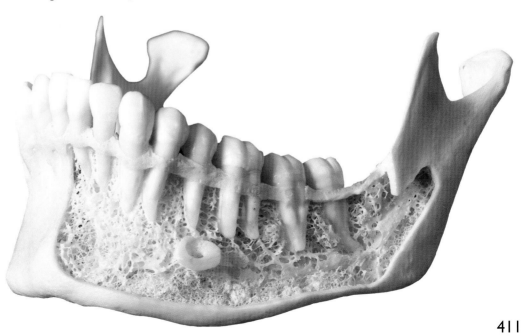

▶ *A cutaway of a human lower jaw shows the roots of the teeth anchored deep in the bone.*

Before the filling can be packed in, the infected parts of the tooth must be drilled out to a shape that allows the filling to be secure when it hardens. The drilled cavity is cleaned with warm water, dried with air, and a protective cement lining is applied. The filling is then plugged in tightly and left to harden. When it is hard, it is carved to the shape of the rest of the tooth.

When the decay has reached the pulp, the dentist may perform root canal therapy. In this case, the pulp is drilled out, even from the canals that extend into the roots, and it is replaced with a rubbery material. While this prevents blood flow into the pulp canal, enough nutrients diffuse into the dentine from the socket to keep the tooth alive. Root therapy generally requires that the tooth receive an artificial crown to protect it.

Crowning and artificial teeth

When a large part of the tooth has been lost, the dentist can fit a "cap" or crown. The usual materials for crowns are gold or ceramics such as porcelain. If gold is used, it has to be mixed with other materials to make it harder. The crown is cemented into place.

When the teeth are so badly affected or damaged that they have to be extracted (removed), false teeth (dentures) can be fitted. When necessary, a fixed "bridge" can be provided. This secures one or more false teeth to the natural teeth for support.

When many or all of the teeth have been lost, dentures can be fitted. The artificial teeth are mounted on a plate that is molded to the shape of the mouth. To do this, a soft claylike material is pressed over the teeth and gums. After a few moments the material sets hard and is taken out.

▶ **This illustration shows how a dentist fills a decayed tooth.**

1. The dark area of decay in the center has penetrated the outer layer (enamel) of the tooth and gone through into the dentine, the inner core of the tooth.

2. The dentist has drilled a hole, removing all the decay. A filling cannot be put in, however, as it would not stick to the tooth and so would fall out.

3. The dentist must shape the hole or cavity in the tooth to give it an undercut, so that it is wider at the bottom than at the top.

4. The filling material is inserted. The dentist checks that the patient bites on it satisfactorily. When the filling sets hard, the undercut holds it firmly in place.

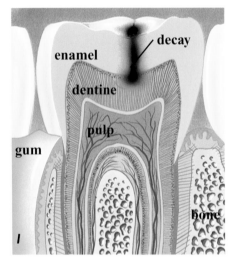

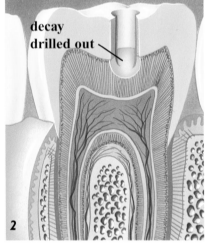

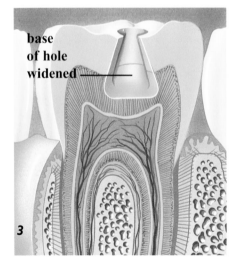

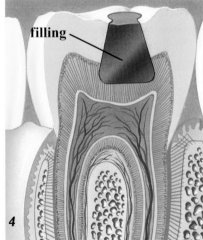

The impression in the material is an exact replica of the inside of the mouth. A creamy mix of plaster is poured into the impression, and when this sets hard it is a model of the mouth. From this cast the dentures can be made and fitted. Materials used for dentures include gold, plastics, and stainless steel.

Gum disease

Diseases of the gums are usually caused by improper care of teeth and gums. Sugars and bacteria build up between the teeth and form plaque. This plaque irritates the gums and causes swelling and bleeding. If this first stage is neglected, hard tartar builds up between the teeth and the gums. In time, this causes the teeth to loosen and they may be lost. Eventually, if the condition is untreated, the bone that supports the teeth can be destroyed. Correct brushing from an early age and frequent visits to the dentist can prevent gum disease. Older people lose more teeth through gum disease than from decay.

Modern dentistry techniques

Modern dentistry methods cause minimal pain to the patient. Teeth that would have been lost to decay or disease can often be saved. Instead of drilling, many dentists now use lasers to burn off decay. To treat gum disease, lasers can be aimed into pockets between the teeth and gums, killing the bacteria that grow there. Previously, an old treatment was to cut away the loose gum. If gums still need to be cut away now, they can be replaced with tissue cut from the roof of the mouth.

Destroyed bone can be replaced by transplanting bone from somewhere else in the patient's body. Another procedure uses freeze-dried bone from other people. This is less likely to be rejected by the patient's immune system.

Teeth that have been knocked out can be replaced. The tooth should be placed in milk to protect it and taken with the patient to the dentist. Lost teeth can also be replaced by artificial teeth built into the jaw. The bases of the new teeth are made of titanium, a metal the human body accepts. New teeth are placed in a hole drilled in the jaw. New bone grows around them, holding them in place.

Most important, dentists have found ways to prevent tooth decay. One technique is to apply plastic sealant to the tooth surface. This sealant fills in the tiny pits where food and bacteria can collect.

See *also*: ANESTHETIC • MEDICAL TECHNOLOGY • SURGERY • X-RAY

Desert

Deserts are very dry areas of land. Most deserts are located in hot parts of the world, although some deserts are cold. The plants and animals that live in deserts can survive with little water.

Deserts are the driest places on Earth, and most plants and animals cannot survive in them. About one-fifth of Earth's land is desert. Deserts occur throughout the world, but most are located in warm, tropical regions north and south of the equator. The world's largest desert is the Sahara Desert in North Africa. It occupies about the same land area as the United States. North America has more than 500,000 square miles (1.3 million square kilometers) of desert, including the Great Basin Desert and the Mojave Desert.

Lack of water

About 1 billion tons (907 million tonnes) of rain falls to Earth every minute. However, very little of this rain falls on deserts. Many scientists define a desert as a place where less than 10 inches (25 centimeters) of precipitation falls every year. Precipitation is the collective name given to rain, hail, and snow. A semidesert is a place that gets less than 15 inches (38 centimeters) of precipitation. It is far too hot in most deserts for snow. Although it does hail on occasion, most deserts get moisture through rainfall. This rain does not generally fall at regular intervals throughout the year. Some land does not receive rain for many years on end. Once rain does come, however, a huge amount falls in a short space of time, causing flash floods. These flood waters form temporary rivers, which flow along seasonally dry valleys called wadis or arroyos.

Some deserts receive more rain than others but are just as dry. These deserts are so dry because water is lost faster than it is received. The water may trickle down into the ground or may be evaporated away by the wind and Sun. Since they are always losing more water than they receive, deserts have

▼ *These Tuareg tribesmen are escorting a camel train across the Sahara Desert. Camels are well adapted to life in the desert. They store fat in the humps on their backs so they can survive periods without food or water.*

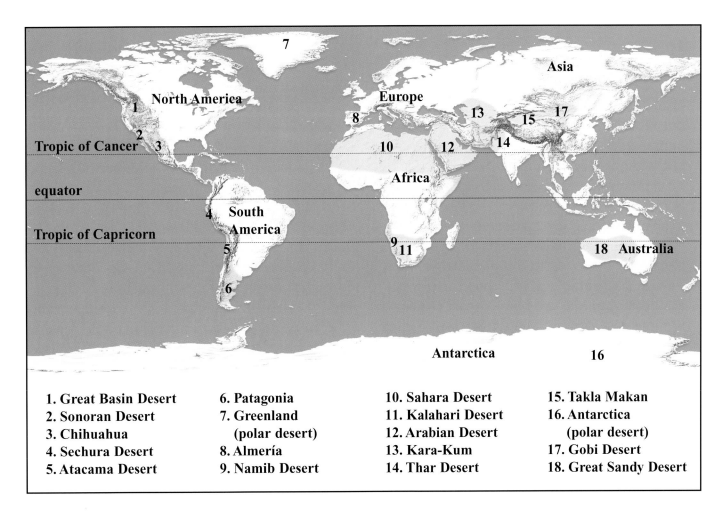

1. Great Basin Desert
2. Sonoran Desert
3. Chihuahua
4. Sechura Desert
5. Atacama Desert

6. Patagonia
7. Greenland
   (polar desert)
8. Almería
9. Namib Desert

10. Sahara Desert
11. Kalahari Desert
12. Arabian Desert
13. Kara-Kum
14. Thar Desert

15. Takla Makan
16. Antarctica
    (polar desert)
17. Gobi Desert
18. Great Sandy Desert

what scientists call a water debt. In contrast, an area of swamp receives more water than it loses and, therefore, has a water surplus.

Wind patterns

Rainfall across the world is affected by the way air moves around. Wind is air flowing from an area of high pressure, where the air molecules are cool and tightly packed, to an area of low pressure, where the molecules are warmer and less tightly packed. As the air moves from areas of high pressure to areas of low pressure, it often carries water vapor with it. When water vapor in the air condenses (turns to liquid), it falls out of the sky as rain.

Most deserts are positioned along the edge of the warm, tropical regions, north and south of the equator. Around the equator, there are no obvious seasons. The Sun is high in the sky all year round. With sunlight beating down day in, day out, the equatorial region is a very warm place. All this heat

▲ *This map shows the world's major desert regions. Deserts along the tropics are largely caused by hot winds blowing from the equator that have run out of moisture. Some other deserts are formed in mountain rain shadows. Polar deserts are areas with little rainfall and where it is so cold that there is no liquid water.*

DID YOU KNOW?

Antarctica is often described as a polar desert. Most of the continent is covered in water in the form of ice. In places, this ice is several miles thick. Animals and plants need liquid water to survive, however, so ice is of no use to them. Like hot deserts, Antarctica rarely receives precipitation. Any rain that does fall soon freezes, so animals and plants cannot use it. Consequently, fewer organisms survive in Antarctica than in even the hottest deserts.

DID YOU KNOW?

New deserts are continually forming in a process called desertification. Climatic changes can be a cause of desertification, but often human activities are to blame. People in already vulnerable arid and semi-arid regions may exhaust surface-water or groundwater supplies for irrigation or human use. They often also allow their animals to overgraze and eat all the plants. Overgrazing will make an area even drier because plant roots hold the soil together, helping it to retain water. When the plants are destroyed, the soil breaks apart, making it impossible for new plants to grow.

makes water from the ocean evaporate into the air. Since warm air rises, this hot, moist air rises up above the equator. As it does so, it begins to cool, and the water vapor in the air condenses and falls as rain. This rain falls on the lush tropical rain forests that grow close to the equator. The cooling air also becomes more dense, making it sink and blow as wind to the north and south, where the air is less dense and lower pressure.

Having dropped its water, the now cooled, sinking air continues to blow away from the equator. As it sinks, the air warms up again, forming a hot, dry wind that reaches the deserts. This wind rarely carries enough moisture for rain clouds to form. The hot air blowing over the land also dries out the soil, evaporating any

▶ *Cacti are common desert plants. They store water in thick, fleshy stems to allow them to survive for long periods without water. To avoid losing water through evaporation, they do not have leaves.*

moisture that might be held in the desert soil. The deserts of northern and southern Africa, such as the Sahara Desert and Kalahari Desert, are formed in this way, as is the Great Australian Desert.

Rain shadow

Deserts do not just form in the hot tropics. Some occur in cooler parts of the world, but these areas are just as dry. Mountain ranges can create deserts because they prevent any moist wind from reaching a region. Air must rise to travel over mountains. As the air travels up the side of the range, it cools and drops its moisture as rain. The wind that flows down the other side of the mountain is much drier, and it rarely brings rain to the land beyond.

This phenomenon is called the rain shadow effect, since the mountains cast a "shadow" where rain does not fall. The Great Basin Desert in the United States is in a rain shadow, between the Sierra Nevada and the Rocky Mountains.

Other deserts form because they are so far from the ocean that rainfall never reaches them. One example is the Gobi Desert, which covers parts of China and Mongolia. The winds that blow over this land are very dry, because they have already dropped any moisture they may have been carrying nearer to the coast.

There are deserts on the coast, however. The Atacama Desert on the coast of Peru and Chile, for example, is surprisingly the driest place on Earth despite being next to the ocean. Coastal deserts form

▲ *The fennec fox spends most of the day in its burrow to avoid the fierce Sun. It comes out to hunt at dawn and dusk, using its excellent hearing to help locate prey.*

because of cold ocean currents running along the coast. The cold water chills the air above it. Since cold air carries less water vapor, the chilly winds that blow to the shore are very dry.

The Sahara Desert is the world's largest desert, stretching right across North Africa. It is so big because it has formed for not one but three reasons. North Africa is at the northern edge of the tropical zone, so the land receives only hot dry winds. Much of the Sahara Desert is also many hundreds of miles from the ocean, so rain-bearing winds rarely reach there. Also, the coast of the western Sahara Desert has a relatively cold ocean current running along it, which prevents wet winds from blowing on shore. All these factors combine to make the Sahara Desert the huge, desolate territory that it is.

Desert life

Surviving in a desert is very hard. Without a blanket of rain clouds over them, deserts get very hot during the day but can plunge to below freezing by night. The difference between day and night temperatures can be as much as 140°F (70°C). All organisms have a lot of water in their bodies. To survive in a desert, they must first find the water that they need, and then hold on to as much of the water as possible in the intense heat.

Although the most familiar desert landscape is one of rolling sand dunes, most deserts are covered in rocks and gravel. It is not easy for plants to grow in either type of ground, as water soaks straight through. Many desert plants have huge networks of roots to collect any water that trickles through the soil. The mesquite trees that grow in the Sonoran Desert in Mexico, for example, have roots that grow 260 feet (80 meters) down. Once they have water, plants need to store it. Many, such as cacti, store water inside fleshy stems covered in a thick, waxy coat. Since plants lose water from their leaves through evaporation, most desert plants have either very small leaves or none at all. Others sprout into life only on the rare occasions that rain falls. They grow and reproduce quickly before the land dries out again, leaving seeds to wait for the next rainstorm.

Many desert animals never drink liquids. They get all the water they need from their food. Most desert animals are active during the night. During the day, they rest in cool burrows. Some frogs and snakes lie dormant in their burrows for months, coming to the surface only when rain falls. Some frogs keep themselves moist underground inside a fluid-filled skin bag.

Larger desert animals survive desert extremes by storing the food they need. For example, camels store fat in their humps. The breakdown of fat produces both energy and water, allowing camels to travel long distances without drinking or eating. Small desert rodents keep food stores stocked with seeds to see them through lean times.

See also: RAIN AND RAINFALL • WATER CYCLE

Diamond

Diamond is one of the most beautiful, rarest, and sought after jewels. It is also very important in industry. Diamond is the hardest known substance on Earth, and this property makes it useful as an industrial tool for cutting and polishing different materials.

Diamonds were formed millions of years ago in molten lava. The lava flowed to Earth's surface, cooled, and grew solid in a rock called kimberlite. Kimberlite occurs in round rock formations called pipes, which vary in size from a few feet across to several hundred acres. At first, kimberlite is gray-blue in color, when it is known as blue ground. After being exposed to the weather, it turns into a yellow clay, called yellow ground. Diamonds are usually mined from kimberlite pipes.

It is estimated that in two hundred years only about 230 tons (208 tonnes) of diamonds have been mined. To get to these diamonds, around

▼ *Rough diamonds come in a great variety of shapes and colors, as this selection shows.*

6 billion tons (5.4 billion tonnes) of rock, sand, and gravel have been moved. Most diamonds come from Africa—South Africa is especially rich in diamond deposits. Originally, diamonds were all mined by simple open-pit methods. The greatest depth ever reached by an open-pit mine was about 800 feet (240 meters) at Kimberley, South Africa. Today, most diamonds are mined in deep underground mines. The shaft of the Kimberley Mine is now 3,500 feet (1,067 meters) deep.

Recovering the diamonds

Diamonds must be recovered from the kimberlite rock undamaged. The first step is to carefully crush the kimberlite to free any diamonds. Then the rock goes through several gravity-separation devices, such as washing pans. The separated material is then passed over a grease table or grease belt, with plenty of water. Diamonds from the kimberlite stick to the grease because water does not wet them easily. Water readily wets the other heavy minerals, so they wash off the grease table. The diamonds caught in the grease are scraped off the table and boiled in water to remove the grease.

Synthetic diamonds

Until 1955, all diamonds were recovered from mines. In that year, artificial diamonds were made at the General Electric plant in Schenectady, New York.

Diamonds are made from carbon. There are two main kinds of carbon crystals: graphite (the "lead" in pencils) and diamond. During the nineteenth century, many people tried to convert graphite into diamond. In 1955, scientists at the General Electric plant succeeded. They subjected carbon to huge pressures (97,000 times atmospheric pressure) and temperature (more than 3600°F or 2000°C) to achieve this. This first attempt produced 40 small stones. Since then, artificial diamonds have been made in many countries. Chemically, these stones are exactly the same as natural diamonds, but they are small and appear pale gold or gray-black.

▶ *This is a diamond mine at Elizabeth Bay, Namibia. The diamonds there do not need to be dug from great depths because they are in alluvial deposits near Earth's surface. The diamonds were eroded from seams farther south, swept into the sea, then carried north by the Benguela Current to the Namibian coast.*

Industrial diamonds

The industrial use of diamonds is not new. The ancient Romans used diamonds for engraving. By the nineteenth century, diamond drills and lathe tools had been invented. Today, 70 million carats of diamond are used in industry each year. One carat is a weight of 0.007 ounces (200 milligrams). The word *carat* is believed to have come from the carob bean, which consistently weighs around the same.

Diamonds are the world's most important abrasive. Diamonds can be crushed and graded into different sizes and shapes for different jobs. About 75 percent of all industrial diamonds are used as abrasive powder. Diamond powder mixed with ceramics, metals, or resins form the cutting surfaces of bandsaws, drills, files, grinding wheels, saw blades, and many other tools used to cut or shape materials, such as concrete, glass, metals, and stone. As a polishing powder, the diamond powder mix gives a fine finish.

Diamond cutting

Very few diamonds are perfect when taken from the ground. Most contain spots and other fine flaws. The position and size of these flaws is very important in the art of diamond cutting. Although it is the hardest natural substance, a diamond can be cut and shaped. It has planes (angles) of weakness, along which it can be cut (cleaved) cleanly in two, if expertly handled.

There are four processes in making diamond gemstones: cleaving, sawing, bruting, and then polishing. Cleaving is used to shape diamonds or to split a very large diamond into smaller pieces. The first shaping of a diamond is often done with a thin phosphor-bronze saw that rotates at about 5,000 revolutions per minute. Bruting is a rounding process, which is carried out before polishing

The most widely used diamond cut is called the brilliant cut, which gives the diamond its greatest shine. It has 58 faces (facets), 33 of which are above the widest part of the diamond and 25 below. A large diamond can take a month to polish. Other popular cuts are the emerald, marquise, oval, and pear. There is now a machine that polishes diamonds up to half a carat with great efficiency. Lasers can be used to drill holes in the stones.

See also: ABRASIVE • CARBON • CRYSTAL • DRILL

Diesel engine

The diesel engine was invented in 1897 by German engineer Rudolf Diesel (1853–1913). One year later, the first diesel engine built in the United States started making power for the Anheuser-Busch Brewery in St. Louis. Diesel engines are now used to power automobiles, locomotives, ships, and many industrial machines.

During World War I (1914–1918), diesel engines were developed for use in submarines. The first successful diesel engines for land vehicles were used in 1922. Then in 1929 came diesels that were specifically designed to power small boats. These engines were later adapted for use in road vehicles.

By the start of World War II (1939–1945), the diesel engine was accepted as the engine of choice for heavy-duty transportation. In addition to their reliability, diesel engines are cheaper to run than gasoline engines. They use less expensive fuel and convert more energy into useful work.

How diesel engines work

Gasoline and diesel engines have a lot in common. Like the gasoline engine, the diesel engine is an internal combustion engine. Fuel is burned inside the engine to provide energy. In a typical internal combustion engine, a mixture of fuel and air explodes in a cylinder. The explosion forces a piston along the cylinder, producing a turning motion of a crankshaft. Usually, several pistons and cylinders provide a smooth turning motion. The fuel-air mixture explodes in the cylinders in rapid succession, so each piston in turn powers the engine. This arrangement increases the engine's power.

▶ *Four diesel locomotives pull a freight train in California. Diesel engines are a powerful and economical alternative to gasoline engines.*

The main difference between a gasoline engine and a diesel engine is the way in which the fuel is mixed with air and ignited. In a gasoline engine, the fuel is mixed with air before it enters the cylinder. In a diesel engine, air is drawn into the cylinder first, and the fuel is sprayed in later.

The fuel-air mixture in a gasoline engine is ignited by means of an electric spark. This is not necessary in a diesel engine. Before the fuel is injected into the cylinder of a diesel engine, the air is compressed by the piston. The high compression makes the temperature of the air rise to well over 1000°F (540°C). When the fuel is injected, the high temperature causes the mixture to explode spontaneously, without the need for a spark.

The volume of air drawn into the cylinder of a diesel engine is always the same. The amount of fuel that is injected can be varied to control the speed at which the engine runs.

Fuel injection

A diesel engine can be adjusted to run on different fuels, from vegetable oils to natural gas and gasoline. However, the most widely used diesel fuel is distilled from crude oil and is similar to kerosene. In the engine, a pump forces the fuel through an injector nozzle at the top of each cylinder. Some engines have separate pumps supplying each injector nozzle. In other designs, one main pump supplies each nozzle in turn through a device called a distributor valve. The pump itself is operated by a spring-loaded plunger, which is moved in and out by a cam mounted on a shaft turned by the engine.

A recent development is the common-rail diesel engine. Common-rail engines work by storing fuel under pressure in a rail that links all the injectors. High-pressure valves control the amount of fuel delivered to each injector. The process of storing the fuel in the rail ensures that it is permanently available at very high pressure to the injectors, regardless of the speed at which the engine is running (which determines the pump rate). This high pressure creates a fine mist of fuel in the combustion chamber, which burns more efficiently with greater performance and reduced emissions.

▲ *This portrait of Rudolf Diesel was taken around 1910. Diesel's engines now power more than half the world's ships and a large proportion of automobiles, railroad locomotives, and tractor trailers.*

The accelerator control of a simple diesel engine is connected to the pump mechanism. Adjusting the control changes the amount of fuel that the pump supplies to the injector nozzles, thus altering the engine speed. In a common-rail engine, the accelerator is connected electronically to the rail's valves, which control fuel flow to the injectors.

Combustion chambers

To burn correctly, the fuel and air must be thoroughly mixed. One way of doing this is to churn up the air being compressed in the cylinder with particular shaping of the top of the piston.

Some diesel engines have a more complex means of mixing the fuel and air. They use an additional combustion chamber connected to the cylinder. One technique is to use a swirl chamber, which is a

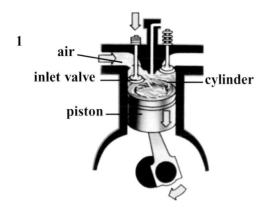

1

air

inlet valve

cylinder

piston

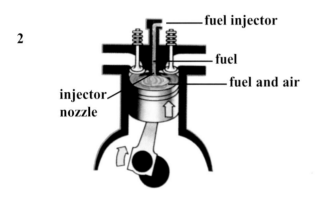

2

fuel injector

fuel

fuel and air

injector nozzle

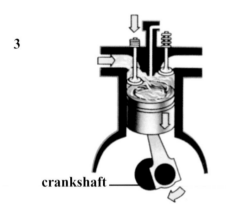

3

crankshaft

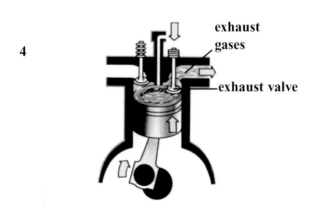

4

exhaust gases

exhaust valve

◄ *This illustration shows the stages in the cycle of a four-stroke diesel engine.*
1. Intake: The falling piston sucks air into the cylinder through the open inlet valves. The valve then shuts.
2. Compression: The piston rises and compresses the air, making it hot. Fuel enters through the injector nozzle.
3. Ignition: The high temperature ignites the fuel-air mixture. The resulting explosion forces the piston down to turn the crankshaft.
4. Exhaust: The exhaust valve opens. The turning crankshaft moves the piston up to push out the exhaust gases.

small, round chamber with a passage linking it to the cylinder. When the air in the cylinder is compressed, some of it is forced through the passage and into the swirl chamber. The shape of the swirl chamber agitates the air so that it mixes well with the fuel when it is injected. The mixture starts to burn, and it expands into the cylinder, where complete combustion takes place.

In other diesel engines, a precombustion chamber is used instead of a swirl chamber. It is connected to the cylinder by several passages. As before, air is forced into the chamber, and fuel is injected. Part of the mixture in the chamber ignites and expands, forcing the rest of the fuel through the connecting passages. The fuel enters the cylinder as a fine spray and burns smoothly.

Supercharging

A technique called supercharging is often used to increase the power of internal combustion engines. It is a means of increasing the amount of fuel and air that can be burned in a cylinder.

In an ordinary diesel engine, air is drawn into a cylinder when the piston moves down. With the addition of a compressor called a supercharger, more air is forced into the cylinders than could be drawn in by the downward motion of the pistons alone. With extra air present, more fuel can be burned in the cylinders and, consequently, the power of the engine increases.

Like fuel pumps, most superchargers are driven directly by the diesel engine. A turbocharger is a supercharger driven by a small turbine—a fanlike device, which is turned by the engine's exhaust gases. The diesel engine is particularly suited to supercharging because the compressor has only to force extra air into the cylinders. Supercharging a gasoline engine is more complex as the air is mixed with fuel before it enters the cylinders.

Starting a diesel engine

Diesel engines with fuel injected directly into the cylinders are usually easy to start. The engine is turned by means of a hand crank or with an electric motor. This ensures that the pistons move in their cylinders, and it also makes the pump supply fuel to the nozzles. The engine soon bursts into life and continues turning under its own power.

Hand starting is easy with smaller diesel engines, but larger models are difficult to hand crank. Consequently, large diesel engines are usually started by means of an electric motor. In some cases, a small, easily started diesel engine is used as a starter for a larger engine.

▼ *This tractor trailer in Kununurra, Western Australia, is powered by a diesel engine, as are most large trucks. Diesel engines are cheaper to run than gasoline engines and produce more power at lower engine speeds. They are therefore useful for pulling big loads.*

Diesel engines that are fitted with swirl chambers or precombustion chambers are also sometimes difficult to start. To help the fuel vaporize when the engine is cold, electrical heaters called glow plugs are often fitted in the chambers.

Uses of diesel engines

Diesel engines are useful for powering heavy vehicles and machines on construction sites and farms. On the railroads, many locomotives are powered by diesel or diesel-electric engines. At sea, diesel engines are used to power various kinds of craft, from small fishing boats to large ocean liners. Diesel engines are also becoming increasingly popular for powering automobiles, particularly in countries where gasoline is comparatively expensive. Diesel engines are more economical to run than gasoline engines and are more reliable for heavy work. For this reason, they are popular with those who cover a high mileage. Many taxis, for example, are fitted with diesel engines.

See also: AUTOMOBILE • ELECTRIC MOTOR • INTERNAL COMBUSTION ENGINE

Digestive system

Before the body can use the food a person eats, the food must first be broken down into simpler substances. This breaking-down process is called digestion. Digestion begins as soon as the food passes into the mouth and ends when waste is passed out of the body through the anus.

Digestion begins when food enters the mouth. As the teeth chew food, the food is broken down into smaller pieces. Saliva in the mouth mixes with the food pieces, making them easy to swallow. Saliva enters the mouth when people think about food or when food is placed in the mouth.

Food passes from the mouth down a tube called the esophagus into the stomach. The esophagus is lined with rings of muscle called sphincters. The food is squeezed down the esophagus by waves of muscular contraction. This muscular squeezing is called peristalsis, and it pushes food all the way down through the digestive system. Peristalsis works all the time, and it does not rely on gravity. Therefore, people can eat while standing on their heads, and astronauts can eat in space.

The stomach

The stomach is a J-shaped bag that acts as a store for the food people eat. It is also the place where various chemicals start to break down food. The stomach has a muscular wall that causes a churning action. The churning breaks up the food and mixes it thoroughly with digestive chemicals. The food is mixed up to become a liquid called chyme.

▼ *Everyone must eat a healthy, balanced diet of foods containing carbohydrates, fats, and proteins, as well as fiber, minerals, vitamins, and water.*

THE DIGESTIVE TRACT

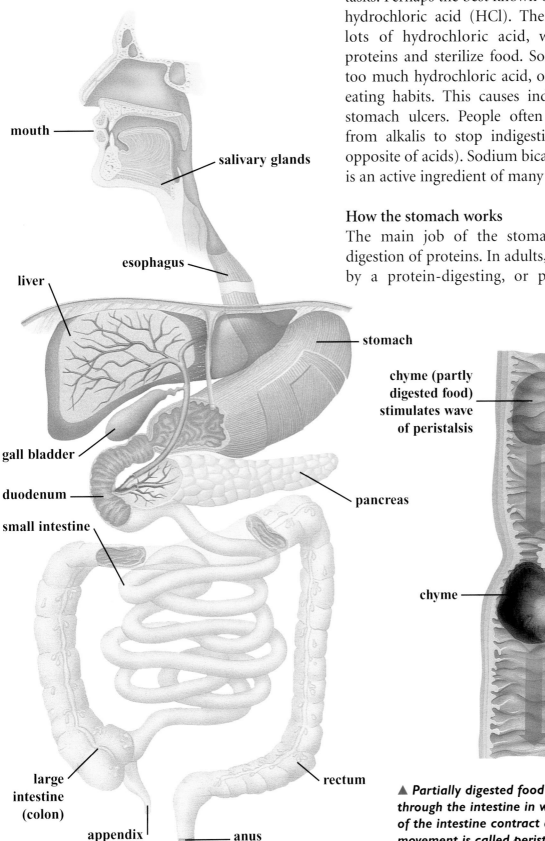

- mouth
- salivary glands
- esophagus
- liver
- gall bladder
- duodenum
- small intestine
- stomach
- pancreas
- large intestine (colon)
- appendix
- rectum
- anus
- chyme (partly digested food) stimulates wave of peristalsis
- chyme

All the chemicals in the stomach have particular tasks. Perhaps the best known of these chemicals is hydrochloric acid (HCl). The stomach produces lots of hydrochloric acid, which helps digest proteins and sterilize food. Some people produce too much hydrochloric acid, often because of bad eating habits. This causes indigestion and often stomach ulcers. People often take tablets made from alkalis to stop indigestion (alkalis are the opposite of acids). Sodium bicarbonate ($NaHCO_3$) is an active ingredient of many indigestion tablets.

How the stomach works

The main job of the stomach is to start the digestion of proteins. In adults, this is done mainly by a protein-digesting, or proteolytic, enzyme

▲ *Partially digested food (chyme) moves through the intestine in waves as the walls of the intestine contract and then relax. This movement is called peristalsis. It is stimulated by the presence of food in the esophagus.*

Follow a few simple rules to help the digestive system to work properly.
1. Chew food well before swallowing it. The digestion of carbohydrates starts with saliva in the mouth.
2. Do not eat food too quickly, because this may result in indigestion.
3. Try to include foods that contain lots of fiber, such as bran, fruit with the skin on, and lightly cooked vegetables. Fiber does not get digested, but it helps the passage of food through the large intestine.
4. Do not drink too much when eating a meal. Liquids dilute digestive juices.
5. Do not eat too much food, because this puts a strain on the digestive system.
6. Try to eat smaller amounts of food regularly than eat too much food at once.

called pepsin. However, the food does not stay in the stomach long enough to be digested completely. The inside of the stomach itself is protected from pepsin and hydrochloric acid by a coating of mucus that forms a barrier between the stomach wall and the chemicals. If there is not enough mucus, the pepsin and acid begin to eat into the stomach wall, resulting in a gastric ulcer.

It takes the stomach between two and six hours to break down food and get rid of the contents. Foods rich in carbohydrates are first to leave the stomach. These include bread, potatoes, rice, and sugar. Then foods rich in proteins leave the stomach. These include cheese, eggs, and meat. Fatty foods stay in the stomach the longest.

Following the partial digestion of food in the stomach, the food passes into the small intestine. In the small intestine, food is digested completely, and the digested food is absorbed into the bloodstream through small villi in the intestine walls. Undigested food goes to the large intestine, where water is absorbed into the body. The waste material is expelled through the anus.

The small intestine

The stomach does very little to absorb foods into the bloodstream. The main breakdown of food and absorption processes takes place in the small intestine, which is about 21 feet (6.4 meters) long. Food stays in the small intestine for many hours. Tubes connect the liver and the pancreas to the small intestine. They pour fluids that further aid digestion through these tubes. Fluid from the pancreas is called pancreatic juice. Fluid from the liver is called bile. Bile is stored in the gall bladder, which is a small bag just under the liver.

While food is in the small intestine, it is further diluted by intestinal juices, which contain enzymes that help digest food. The juices are produced at a rate of about 5 to 10 quarts (4.7 to 9.4 liters) every day. When food in the small intestine is completely digested, it is absorbed into tiny blood and lymph vessels in the walls of the small intestine. It then goes into the bloodstream to nourish every cell that makes up the body. Food can pass into the bloodstream only when it is completely digested.

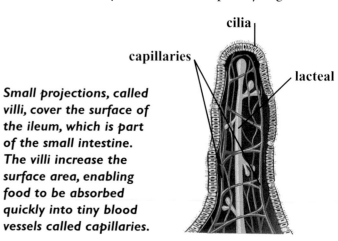

Small projections, called villi, cover the surface of the ileum, which is part of the small intestine. The villi increase the surface area, enabling food to be absorbed quickly into tiny blood vessels called capillaries.

cilia

capillaries

lacteal

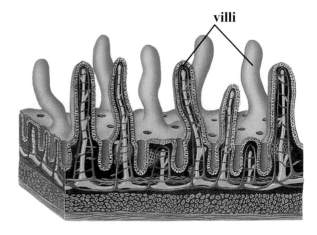

villi

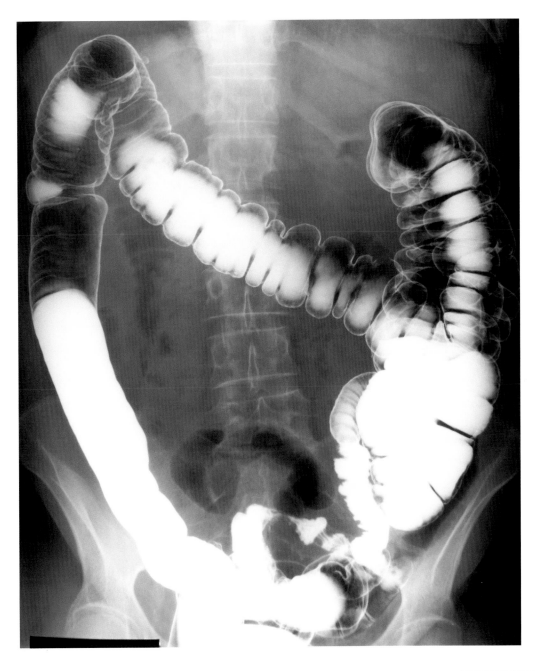

◄ *The large intestine shows up as a pale tube in this X-ray image. Undigested food enters the large intestine, and water and salt are absorbed by the lining of the intestinal wall. The residue forms feces, which are expelled through the anus.*

Food that is still undigested moves into the large intestine. Very little digestion takes place in the large intestine, and the food moves very slowly. Although it is only about 5 feet (1.5 meters) long, it takes the undigested remains of food between 10 and 20 hours to pass through the large intestine. The main job of the large intestine is to remove water from the undigested material. Salt is also absorbed by the lining of the large intestine. The waste, together with dead cells and bacteria, is pressed into solids called feces and then passed out of the body through the anus.

DID YOU KNOW?

Despite its many tasks, the stomach is not absolutely necessary. There have been cases where people have been able to live without a stomach. However, this puts a strain on the rest of the digestive system.

See also: CARBOHYDRATE • CIRCULATORY SYSTEM • EXCRETORY SYSTEM • FAT • PROTEIN

Digital audio software

Music can be stored on computers as digital audio files. The most common audio file used today is MP3, but there are several other types. Whereas compact discs (CDs) and other music formats have to be bought in shops, digital audio files can be transferred between computers using the Internet. The files can also be downloaded onto smaller personal players, which can be used to listen to music anywhere.

In the same way as text and pictures are saved in a computer's memory, music and other sounds can be stored as audio files. Computers have been saving and playing back sounds for more than 20 years. Until recently, however, the quality of the sound saved in audio files was not very good. People preferred to listen to their favorite songs played on compact disc (CD) or minidisc. In recent years, it has become possible to save high-quality sound as digital audio files. These files are available in several formats, perhaps the most familiar being MP3. MP3s and other similar files produce sound that is nearly as good as music played directly from a CD. However, they take up less than a tenth of the amount of computer memory, making it easier to store files and send them through the Internet.

Digital codes

All computer files, including audio ones, are digital. The files are coded as a long list of 1s and 0s. A computer's processor decodes this list to recreate whatever has been saved. The computer uses the 0s and 1s in an audio file as "on" or "off" switches to

control its many electrical circuits and reproduce the sound. In the real world, however, things are not produced using digital codes. Real things, including sounds, are analog. They are created by increasing or decreasing something rather than switching it on or off.

For example, the sound of a voice consists of a series of air vibrations. These are made in the throat and mouth and are then detected by the ears. Louder noises are produced by bigger air vibrations. Smaller ones make quieter noises. Many vibrations produced in quick succession make high-pitched noises. Vibrations produced less often, or at a lower frequency, make deeper sounds. A person's voice therefore is an analog signal made up of vibrations of varying sizes and frequencies.

Sampling

In any form of electronic sound recording, a microphone or a set of microphones converts the sound wave into an electronic signal, a voltage in a circuit that varies rapidly with time. In digital recording, the circuit samples this voltage many thousands of times and records the resulting set of voltages in digital form—as strings of 0s and 1s. When the sound is played back, the reverse process occurs—a circuit converts the string of numbers into a time-varying voltage that can be played through a speaker. The circuit is designed to ignore an occasional error in the numbers, so that the playback version is relatively free of noise.

Digital sampling was first developed for recording sound onto CDs more than 20 years ago. A three-minute pop song takes up about 32 megabytes (MB) on a CD. There is capacity for approximately 20 of these audio files on a CD, and room for about 300 on an average personal computer (PC). However, there would be no room for anything else in the computer's memory, including the software needed to play the music, if 300 songs were stored on a PC.

◀ *This man is downloading music files from the Internet onto his handheld MP3 player.*

▲ *Portable MP3 players, such as this Rio Sport model, are a popular way of listening to music. Since music files can be stored on a microchip, MP3 players are much smaller than other portable music devices.*

Compression

MP3s and other digital audio files, such as WAV, AIFF, and others, compress the sampled information so it takes up much less space on a computer's hard disk. Compressing music files

DID YOU KNOW?

The name *MP3* comes from the people who designed the way the system works. The Moving Picture Experts Group (MPEG) are computer scientists. Their MPEG Audio Layer-3 file format has now been shortened to just MP3. As well as developing MP3s, MPEG also figured out how to put movies on DVDs and transmit high-definition television pictures (HDTV).

makes it practical to store many hundreds of different songs. Small files are also much easier to copy from one computer to another, or from a computer onto a small personal player. Personal audio players are designed to play just music stored as audio files. They are much smaller and lighter than a computer and can be used to listen to music just about anywhere.

Compression is done using complicated sets of calculations called algorithms. The algorithms work in several ways to keep the amount of information stored to a minimum. One method of compression involves removing the sections of a

song that are repeated. For example, a person singing a ten-note scale up and down five times sings 50 notes in all. But they are also repeating the same ten notes five times. Instead of including all 50 notes, a compressed file saves the ten notes and remembers in which order they should be replayed. This system requires much less code. This sort of compression is not unique to MP3s or other digital audio files. However, MP3s are also created using a unique type of compression called "perceptual noise shaping." This compression system takes into account how the human ear can detect some sounds better than others. For example, when two musical instruments are played at once, one is often drowned out by the other. This is taken into account when an MP3 file is produced. Only the sound that a human ear will be able to detect is saved, and the inaudible sounds are all removed from the code.

Music revolution

Digital audio files are beginning to change the way people listen to and buy music. Before MP3s made it easy to store high-quality sounds on a computer, people generally bought their music prerecorded on tapes or CDs. Some of the money the purchaser paid for the CD went to the artists who wrote and performed the songs. Although it is possible to make copies of store-bought music and save them

▲ *Apple's iPod portable MP3 player contains a compact hard drive that can store many thousands of tunes as MP3 files.*

▶ *Special music software such as Apple's iTunes is used to download, organize, and play digital music files on a computer.*

on CDs or tapes, it is illegal to sell these "pirate" copies or even give them away. This law protects the rights of the writers and artists.

MP3s have changed all that forever. Many people are now copying the music they bought onto MP3 players, so they can listen to it when they are away from home. MP3 players work in one of two ways. Some store the music on microchips. Examples include Internal Flash memory, CompactFlash and SmartMedia cards, and Memory Sticks. This so-called solid-state memory is a very efficient way of storing information, and players using this technology are very small. Also, because there are no moving parts involved, solid-state MP3 players are very reliable and music playback is not prone to skipping if the player is jolted.

However, solid-state memory is an expensive way of storing a lot of files. Where high-capacity storage is needed, people use slightly larger players that contain hard disks. These store information as a magnetic pattern on a spinning disk, and are mini versions of the memory inside computers.

Music exchanges

Copying store-bought music to MP3 players and computers is not against the law, since it is for personal use. However, it is so simple and fast to create digital files from CDs that distributing the copied music is now easier than ever, although still illegal. Copying music to a CD or tape can take a

▲ *For a small fee, it is now possible to hook up to a Music Teller station in a record store. After selecting the music of his choice, this man will download the digital music file onto his MP3 music player.*

long time, and every copy made takes the same amount of time. MP3 files can be copied in seconds and sent around the world to hundreds of people in minutes by e-mail.

In the late 1990s, music exchange Web sites appeared on the Internet. These sites allowed people to download MP3 files of songs made by people they had never met. Soon millions of people were getting hold of music in this way, but they were not paying the artist who created the music in the first place. Many of these Web sites were forced to shut down by the music industry, or they now charge people for downloading music. Just like in a store, some of the money paid for a song goes to the artist who created it.

DID YOU KNOW?

In the near future, people will be able to buy their favorite music as audio files. They will not have to go into a shop to do this. Instead, they can go to their nearest music teller. This ATM-like machine will be able to transmit MP3s or other audio files to a digital music player. The price of each song will depend on how popular it is and for how long someone wants to keep it on their player.

See also: ELECTRONICS • SOFTWARE

Dinosaur

The largest land animals to have ever walked on Earth were the dinosaurs. The dinosaurs lived in the Mesozoic Era, between 230 and 65 million years ago. Dinosaurs were reptiles, but their closest living relatives are not snakes or lizards, but birds. Dinosaurs are known for their large size, though not all of them were giants. The dinosaurs died in a mass extinction event that occurred about 65 million years ago.

The largest land animal alive today is the African elephant. These mighty beasts dwarf people. They are nearly three times as tall and almost one hundred times as heavy. If elephants had existed during the age of the dinosaurs, it would have been the elephants that seemed small. One of the largest dinosaurs, *Brachiosaurus*, would have been more than ten times the size of the largest elephant. Even small dinosaurs would look large today.

Dinosaurs were a large group of reptiles that dominated life on Earth for more than 160 million years. Humans have been on Earth only for about 200,000 years. The dinosaurs died out 65 million years ago in a mass extinction event. With no dinosaurs left alive, everything scientists know about the dinosaurs comes from studying their fossilized remains.

Dinosaurs were not properly identified until the nineteenth century. People came across their remains much earlier than that, however. The earliest discoveries date back nearly two thousand years to China. These early finds were thought to be the bones of dragons. Native Americans also tell stories about their ancestors uncovering the bones of giant buffalo, but these were probably the remains of dinosaurs, too.

In 1822, Mary Ann Mantell—wife of English obstetrician and amateur geologist Dr. Gideon Mantell (1790–1852)—found some large teeth in a gravel pit in southern England. She showed them to her husband. After a few years of research, Dr. Mantell announced that the tooth must have

▶ *These dinosaur skeletons form part of an exhibition at the American Museum of Natural History in New York. Exhibits such as these reveal to people the enormous size of many dinosaur species.*

shared similarities. Owen named all these similar animals dinosaurs. The word *dinosaur* means "terrible lizard." However, the dinosaurs were not closely related to lizards, and most were not nearly as fierce as Owen's name suggests. Many were gentle plant eaters, although huge by modern standards. However, a few carnivorous (meat-eating) species, such as *Tyrannosaurus rex,* would have been truly terrifying for their size, speed, and killing power.

Types of dinosaurs

Paleontologists are still discovering new dinosaur species. Most new finds occur in Argentina, Australia, and China. Dinosaur bones are found all over the world because when these reptiles first evolved, all Earth's continents were joined together into a single landmass called Pangaea. By the time Pangaea began to break into the continents of today, the dinosaurs had already evolved into a wide range of different species.

The dinosaurs belong to a larger group of reptiles called the archosaurs. The word *archosaur* means "ruling lizard," and it was these animals that

▲ *A paleontologist uncovers the fossilized skull of an* **Albertosaurus,** *a smaller version of* **Tyrannosaurus rex** *that stalked late Cretaceous coastal swamps.*

▶ *British anatomist Richard Owen studied ancient animal remains and was the first person to use the word* **dinosaur.** *Owen was one of the founding members of the Natural History Museum in London.*

belonged to a plant-eating reptile that would have been 40 feet (12 meters) long. He named this reptile *Iguanodon,* meaning "iguana tooth," because the fossilized teeth appeared to be large versions of those of an iguana lizard.

For the next 15 years, people kept finding the remains of similar ancient monsters. For example, footprints were found in rocks in the Connecticut Valley that were 200 million years old. At first, people thought that some sort of ancient bird had made these prints, but it is now known that they were made by a two-legged dinosaur.

In 1840, English anatomist Richard Owen (1804–1892) began to compare the bones that had been discovered. He noticed that many of the fossils

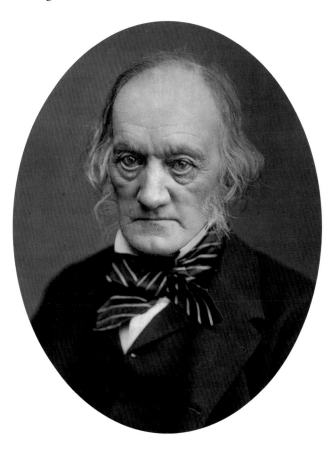

▲ Crocodiles are one of the most ancient animals still living. They evolved with the dinosaurs 200 million years ago, from the reptile group **Archosauria**.

dominated the world during the Age of Reptiles between 230 million to 65 million years ago. As well as the dinosaurs, the archosaurs included flying reptiles called pterosaurs and crocodiles.

Dinosaurs themselves are divided into two orders (groups). The first order is named Saurischia, which means "lizard-hipped." This name refers to the shape of these animals' pelvis bones, which are similar to the pelvis bones of modern-day lizards. The second order is named Ornithischia, which means "bird-hipped." The pelvises of dinosaurs in this order resemble those of birds.

Therapods

The order Saurischia is further divided into two subgroups. The first subgroup is the therapods. This name means "beast feet," and it refers to the fact that all therapods walked on just two legs, and most were fierce hunters. Therapods included some of the more familiar dinosaurs, for example, tyrannosaurs and velociraptors. *Tyrannosaurus rex* is perhaps the most familiar therapod. Its name, which means "king of the tyrant lizards," is well earned. At 40 feet (12 meters) long, *Tyrannosaurus rex* was one of the largest land carnivores that ever walked on Earth. Its head was 4½ feet (1.4 meters) long, and its jaw was armed with teeth that were more than 6 inches (15 centimeters) long. Like most therapods, tyrannosaurs had small forelegs. In the case of tyrannosaurs, these limbs were probably fairly useless appendages. Velociraptors (meaning "rapid grabbers"), on the other hand, had grasping forelimbs armed with razor-sharp claws. These ferocious therapods were smaller than

▲ **Velociraptor** *was a carnivorous dinosaur from the Cretaceous period (99 million to 65 million years ago). Velociraptor used sharp toe claws to kill its prey.*

tyrannosaurs and used stealth and speed to catch their prey. Velociraptors killed with a slash of a long, hooked toe claw on each foot.

Perhaps the most intelligent of all dinosaurs was *Troodon*. This dinosaur was small, reaching only 6 feet (1.8 meters) long, but it had a comparatively large brain. Its brain was still not very large, however, because dinosaurs were generally very unintelligent animals. Nevertheless, *Troodon* was possibly as clever as a small present-day mammal. It

▼ *The giant plant-eating* **Diplodocus** *was a sauropod that lived during the Jurassic period (159 million to 144 million years ago). It was one of the largest ever land animals, weighing up to 80 tons (73 tonnes).*

used its intelligence and sharp eyesight to hunt at night for small mammals. Mammals appeared at the same time as dinosaurs. They did not become anything more than tiny shrewlike animals, however, until the dinosaurs had become extinct.

Sauropods

The second dinosaur subgroup is the sauropods, or Saurischia, meaning "lizard feet." These animals were the largest dinosaurs of all. All were plant eaters that walked on four sturdy legs. They had long necks and small heads, and their long tails were used to balance their necks. Unlike other four-legged reptiles, such as modern-day lizards, sauropods held their bodies off the ground. A lizard or crocodile generally rests it belly on the ground.

The largest sauropods needed to eat vast amounts of food to survive. They had huge stomachs to digest their plant meals. For example, *Brachiosaurus* fed on conifer trees in Africa. Since it had a long neck like a giraffe, it was tall enough to pluck vegetation from the highest branches, out of reach from other animals. Other well-known sauropods were *Apatosaurus*, perhaps better known as *Brontosaurus*, and its smaller relative *Diplodocus*. These giants roamed in herds across present-day North America.

Ornithischia

Five types of dinosaurs are grouped in the order Ornithischia. All of them ate plants. The stegosaurs are best known for the bony plates that ran along their backs. These plates may have been used as armor, or they could have been used to control body temperature. The plates may have absorbed heat from the Sun when the stegosaurs were cold and released heat as required to keep the animals cool.

The plates that covered ankylosaurs were definitely used for armor. Most ankylosaurs had spikes growing on the shoulders and head. A few had bony lumps at the tip of the tail that made formidable clubs.

Ornithopods were the third group in the Ornithischia. They often walked on just their hind feet. Duck-billed dinosaurs were the most common type of ornithopod. These animals had a broad beak covering the mouth. Inside was a jaw filled with teeth. The beak and teeth were used to crush tough plant food. Many duck-billed dinosaurs also had bony crests arching over the head. These crests were connected by air passages to the animals' noses. Some scientists have suggested that the crests were used to make loud, honking calls.

The fourth group in the Ornithischia order was given the name *pachycephalosaurs,* which literally means "thick headed." These two-legged dinosaurs had heavily reinforced skulls, sometimes covered in spikes or ridges. Dinosaur experts have suggested that these dinosaurs would butt their heads together when fighting over food or mates.

The final group in the Ornithischia order is the ceratops, or horned dinosaurs. As their name suggests, most of these animals had horns on the head. These horns were used for defense. The ceratops also had hooked mouths that looked like parrots' beaks and large bony plates that protected the head and neck. *Triceratops* is perhaps the most

DID YOU KNOW?

Before birds appeared, other flying animals filled the skies. The pterosaurs, or "winged lizards," were not dinosaurs, but they did belong to the Archosaur group of reptiles. *Pterosaur* wings were not like the wings of birds. They were more similar to those of bats—flying mammals. The wings were flexible flaps of skin stretched along what was an evolved, highly extended finger.

familiar member of this group. *Triceratops* had a horn on the nose and other horns over each eye. The horns were probably an effective deterrent against hungry tyrannosaurs.

A matter of life and death

Like many other reptiles, dinosaurs laid eggs. In some cases, the parents would have incubated the eggs in a nest before they hatched. Other species would have buried them in a safe place. Scientists do not know whether or not parents cared for their young after they hatched.

Unlike warm-blooded mammals, modern reptiles are all cold-blooded animals. They rely on heat energy from the Sun to warm their bodies. When it is cold, these animals move very slowly. It is likely that most dinosaurs were also cold-blooded animals, although some must have been warm-blooded. Warm-blooded animals can control their own body temperatures internally.

Evidence suggests that plant-eating dinosaurs were probably cold-blooded, but that smaller hunting species could not rely on the weather to warm them up enough before each hunt.

◄ **Triceratops** *was a herbivore from the Cretaceous period. Its bony head crest and large horns provided some a measure of protection against predation.*

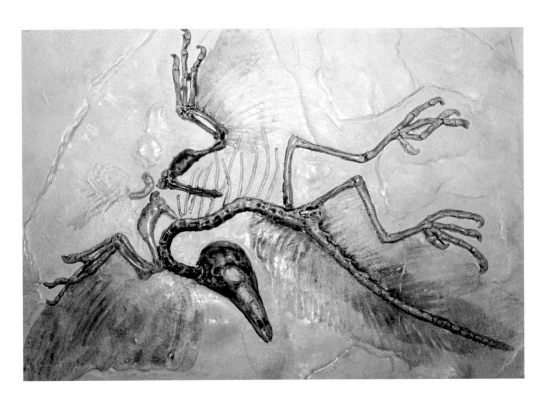

▶ *This picture shows the fossilized remains of Archaeopteryx, an early feathered dinosaur. Scientists think that Archaeopteryx is the ancestor of modern birds.*

The world of the dinosaurs was very different from today. The climate was slightly warmer and changed less throughout the year. Most of the plants were coniferous (cone bearing). Flowering plants did not appear until 100 million years ago.

By around 65 million years ago, most of the dinosaurs and many other animals had disappeared. They may have disappeared because of changes in climate. Scientists know that Earth was becoming cooler and drier at the time, and regional changes would also have occurred as the continents drifted apart. Conifers, the favorite food of many dinosaur species, were also being replaced with flowering plants. These and other factors would explain the initial decline of dinosaurs, but they finally died out so quickly that there was probably a natural disaster that tipped the balance. It so happens that around that time, a huge meteorite smashed into Earth at Chicxulub off the coast of Mexico. The impact of this collision sent millions of tons of dust into the air, and hot debris set fires across the world. The smoke and dust would have blocked out the Sun's rays for months, if not years, and plants would not be able grow. Without this vital source of food, the many millions of animals on Earth would have died out very quickly.

Life after dinosaurs

With the dinosaurs gone, mammals began to take their place, evolving into the wildlife on Earth today. However, there are other animals alive now that did not exist during the time of dinosaurs. They are the birds. Most biologists believe that birds are directly descended from therapod dinosaurs that survived the mass extinction. Like therapods, birds walk on two legs. They have feet with three main toes, and both animals have characteristic S-shaped necks and wishbones in their chests.

Fossils have been found of feathered animals with wings. The most famous is *Archaeopteryx*, which lived about 140 million years ago. This is the oldest bird fossil yet found. It is likely that feathered dinosaurs, such as *Archaeopteryx,* evolved into birds after millions of years of living in trees. In 2000, remains were found in China of a dinosaur with feathered legs and arms. Named *Microraptor*, it probably glided from tree to tree much like a flying squirrel does. If birds did evolve from tree-living feathered dinosaurs, then the dinosaurs never died out. They are still all around, in the skies above us.

See also: GEOLOGIC TIMESCALE • BIODIVERSITY

Disease

Diseases are medical conditions that have a negative effect on the body or the mind. Some diseases are caused by infectious microorganisms such as bacteria or fungi. Others result from a lack of essential nutrients in the diet. Whatever their cause, hundreds of millions of people worldwide die each year as a result of different diseases.

Diseases are medical conditions that prevent part of the body or mind from working properly. Everyone experiences diseases from time to time, and usually they are not dangerous. In most cases, the body's immune system responds to the disease. With plenty of rest, the symptoms will gradually disappear. Sometimes, people need help from a physician to recover from a disease. In other cases, a disease may be so debilitating to the sufferer that he or she eventually dies. Every year in the United States, two million people die from various diseases.

Every disease has a number of symptoms. A symptom is an effect the disease has on the body. Physicians look at the symptoms of a disease to figure out what is wrong. A common symptom is a high body temperature, or fever. A fever is a result of the body's immune response to the disease. Other common symptoms of diseases include diarrhea, exhaustion, muscular aches, and nausea.

There are two types of disease. Infectious diseases can be passed from one person to another. These diseases are caused by tiny, single-celled micro-organisms such as bacteria or viruses. Influenza is an example of an infectious disease. Noninfectious diseases cannot be passed from one person to another. They may have various causes, or often a combination of many. Generally, noninfectious diseases are caused by nonliving things or by the person's body itself. Breast cancer and migraine are examples of noninfectious diseases.

▲ *Young children are extremely vulnerable to diseases such as common colds and influenza. Adults are better able to cope with these diseases because they have had time to build up immunity to the infectious agents.*

Physicians also define diseases in two other ways. Acute diseases develop quickly, rapidly become much worse, and then the symptoms will either disappear or the sufferer will die. Chronic diseases develop over a long time and produce a low level of symptoms for many years. Many chronic diseases will never go away completely, but physicians can treat the sufferer to reduce the symptoms.

The time and the place

A handful of diseases, such as the common cold, can strike anyone, anywhere, and at any time. Other diseases are more likely to affect people at certain times in their lives. For example, osteoporosis is a degenerative bone disease that normally affects older people. By contrast, young children are much more likely to suffer from chicken pox.

▶ *This boy is suffering from chicken pox infection. The virus that causes chicken pox is transmitted by airborne droplets. About two weeks after infection, a mild fever develops, followed by an itchy rash of red pimples that spread over the body. The pimples turn into blisters and then scabs that drop off after about 12 days.*

Other diseases are restricted to certain parts of the world. Many diseases are confined to the hot, humid tropics. For example, people can catch yellow fever only if they visit tropical regions in Africa and South America. The mosquitoes that carry the fever-causing pathogens live only in these areas. In fact, more diseases occur in the tropics than anywhere else in the world, and some physicians specialize in tropical medicine.

Other regions also have their associated diseases. For example, the ticks that carry the bacteria (*singular,* bacterium) that cause Rocky Mountain spotted fever live only in the Rocky Mountains in North America. Frostbite is a serious risk for people who visit or live in very cold places. Frostbite occurs when the extremities of the body—the fingers, nose, or toes—freeze. Snow blindness is another common condition in cold places. It occurs when sunlight reflected from snow or ice causes an inflammation of the eyes. Climbers may suffer from altitude sickness. This problem occurs in high mountain regions when people cannot breathe in enough oxygen from the thin air.

Bacterial infections

Polite people use a tissue or handkerchief to cover the mouth when they cough or sneeze. They also wash their hands after visiting the restroom. These simple measures stop the spread of disease. Most pathogens are tiny microorganisms that are invisible to the naked eye. They can pass from person to person through the air when people cough or sneeze, or they can contaminate water supplies or food. Some diseases are spread when people have unprotected sex. In a few cases, diseases can be caught by just touching a sufferer.

Most diseases are caused by microorganisms called bacteria. These tiny, single-celled organisms cause disease by feeding on certain parts of the

DID YOU KNOW?

Bovine spongiform encephalopathy (BSE), or mad cow disease, is a fatal brain disease of cattle. BSE originated in Britain in the 1980s. The first case of BSE in the United States was confirmed in December 2003. The symptoms of BSE are similar to those of scrapie, which is a brain disease affecting goats and sheep. There are also similarities with Creutzfeldt-Jakob disease (CJD). This brain disease affects mainly older people. Scientists figured out that BSE developed in cattle after they had eaten food containing the brains of scrapie-infected sheep. When young people started to contract CJD, scientists realized that the brains of BSE-infected cattle may have entered the human food chain in beef products. There is no cure for BSE or CJD, and vets and physicians do not know exactly what causes these diseases. As a preventive measure, however, brain products are no longer used in animal feed or human food.

▲ *This seventeenth-century woodcut shows the terrible consequences of the Black Death epidemic in London in 1665. A town crier (center right) walks down the street, calling out "Bring out your dead" to residents of the street. In the background, the corpses are loaded onto a cart to be driven away and burned.*

DID YOU KNOW?

One of the most deadly diseases in history is bubonic plague, or Black Death. In the past, bubonic plague has killed hundreds of millions of people. In one mass outbreak in Europe between 1347 and 1352, around 25 million people—nearly a quarter of all the people in Europe—lost their lives. The bacterium that causes the disease is called *Yersinia pestis*. It lives in the stomach of a type of flea found on rats. *Yersinia pestis* passes into human blood through the bites of infected fleas. Symptoms of the disease include high fever and painful swellings in the armpits and groin. Bubonic plague can be cured with modern antibiotics such as streptomycin. Left untreated, however, the disease often results in death less than a week after the symptoms first appear.

body or releasing poisonous chemicals called toxins. As the bacteria multiply, the infection and symptoms of the infection get worse.

The most likely place to get a bacterial infection is in the windpipe or intestine, causing a sore throat or an upset stomach. Bacteria also cause problems if they infect cuts in the skin. If the body cannot fight off the infection, a physician will prescribe chemicals called antibiotics, which kill the bacteria.

Viral diseases

Viruses are much simpler than bacteria. Viruses are short strands of deoxyribonucleic acid (DNA) coated in chemicals called proteins. DNA is the genetic blueprint for almost all living organisms.

Viruses cause diseases by invading cells and adding their DNA to the cell's DNA. The viral DNA inside the cell then replicates, making more copies of the virus. Eventually, the cell makes so many new viruses that it bursts. The infected cell dies, and the viruses are released to infect new cells.

The symptoms of a viral disease, such as influenza, result from the body's immune response to the virus. Mucus is produced in the nose to flush out viruses and dead cells, and this may produce symptoms such as sneezing. A fever develops as the immune system kicks into action. Viruses are filtered from the blood by lymph nodes, and these small organs become swollen and tender.

Over time, the immune system can deal with most viral infections. After a few days of discomfort, the sufferer will start to feel much better. There is little a physician can do to treat viral diseases, however, because viruses do not respond to antibiotic treatment. Viruses such as human immunodeficiency virus (HIV)—the virus that causes acquired immunodeficiency syndrome (AIDS)—are harder for the body to tackle. HIV is so effective at infecting the body because it attacks the immune system itself.

Other routes of infection

Some infectious diseases are caused by other types of pathogens. Most are microscopic, but a few are caused by larger animals, such as worms. Several pathogens find their way into their victims through a third animal, called a vector.

Athlete's foot is common fungal disease. This is caused by tiny strands of fungus growing on and under the skin, causing an itchy rash. Sweaty areas, for example, between the toes, are most commonly affected. Scabies is another itchy skin disease. Scabies is caused by mites (tiny relatives of spiders) burrowing through the skin. Tapeworms live inside the intestines, while flukes are flatworms that feed inside the liver and blood vessels.

Many killer diseases are caused by organisms called protists. Many protists resemble bacteria, but they are much bigger. Some protists infect people through an animal vector. For example, protists from the genus (group) *Plasmodium* cause a disease called malaria, which kills more than two million people worldwide each year. *Plasmodium* spreads from person to person through the bites of female *Anopheles* mosquitoes. The mosquitoes pick up *Plasmodium* pathogens when they feed on the

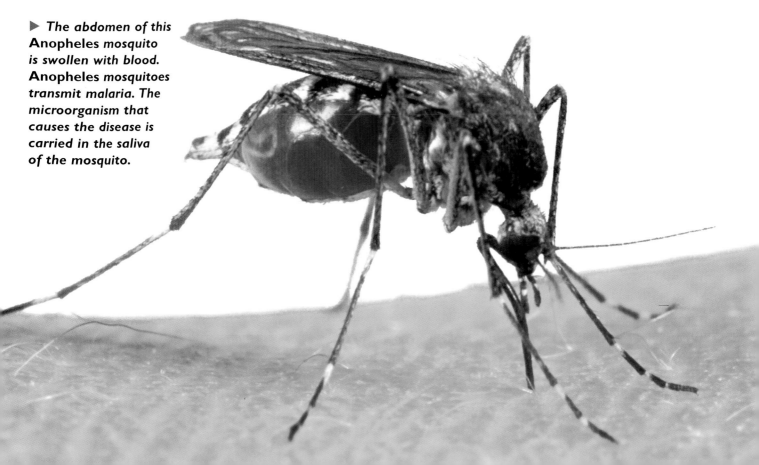

▶ *The abdomen of this* **Anopheles** *mosquito is swollen with blood.* **Anopheles** *mosquitoes transmit malaria. The microorganism that causes the disease is carried in the saliva of the mosquito.*

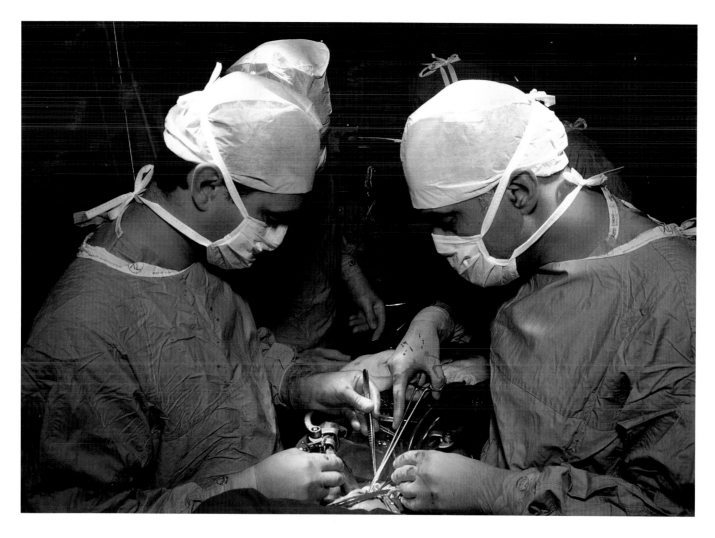

blood of a malaria sufferer. The pathogen then passes into the bloodstream of uninfected people if the mosquito feeds on them.

Other insect vectors include black flies, which spread a disease called river blindness. This disease is caused by tiny roundworms that damage the eyes. Tsetse flies act as vectors for trypanosomes. These protists cause sleeping sickness, which is another dangerous tropical disease.

Noninfectious diseases

Many diseases are not caused by microorganisms and cannot be passed from person to person. Non-infectious diseases have a number of possible causes, for example, environmental pollution, a poor diet, or lifestyle choices such as drinking too much alcohol, smoking, and physical inactivity. Some noninfectious diseases are present from birth; others develop as a person grows older.

▲ *Surgeons perform a heart bypass operation. This operation involves inserting new blood vessels leading to the heart, which bypass arteries that have become clogged with fatty deposits. This type of heart disease is one of the main killers in the United States.*

Cancers are perhaps the most familiar group of noninfectious diseases. A cancer is the uncontrolled growth of body tissue. The growing tissue produces a tumor, which damages healthy tissue as it grows. Eventually, the tumor gets so big that it stops the body from functioning. Cancers have many causes. Some are caused by cancer-causing chemicals called carcinogens. For example, the carcinogens in cigarette smoke cause lung cancer. However, most cancers have no definite cause.

One in every three people are affected by cancer at some point in their lives. Cancer is a very serious disease, but many people are cured and live healthy lives for many years after the problem is discovered.

DID YOU KNOW?

Anthrax is an extremely deadly disease that affects the lungs, stomach, or skin. It is caused by the bacterium *Bacillus anthracis* (shown below). Anthrax in the lungs and stomach is very dangerous, killing most of the people infected in this way. Anthrax in the skin tends to be less deadly. Anthrax bacteria are found throughout the world. Most bacteria exist as toughened, inactive forms, called spores, in the soil. Infection occurs when people inhale or swallow the spores or when they enter a cut or break in the skin. Since anthrax is so deadly, it has been developed as a biological weapon and has been used by terrorists.

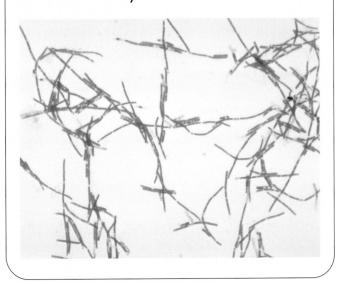

Other common noninfectious diseases include arthritis, heart disease, and stroke. These diseases generally affect older people and are caused by damage to some part of the body. Arthritis affects the joints between bones. Most types of arthritis are caused by wear and tear of bones over many years. Heart disease is caused by blockages in the arteries leading away from the heart and makes people prone to heart attacks. A stroke is brain damage caused by a blood clot. Strokes can be so severe that the victim dies immediately. In most cases, however, the damage produces long-term mental and physical disabilities.

Genetic and long-term diseases

Several diseases run in families. The diseases are passed down through the generations in genes. A genetic defect in the body causes problems from birth. Hemophilia and sickle-cell anemia are common genetic diseases. Both are blood diseases. Hemophiliacs cannot form blood clots very well, so they may bleed to death from the slightest cut. Sickle-cell anemia sufferers have crescent-shaped blood cells that often get stuck in small blood vessels, causing excruciating pain. The blocked blood vessel also makes the sufferer appear pale.

Although they are not present from birth, similar noninfectious diseases can affect people for their entire lives. For example, diabetes is a disease suffered by people who cannot regulate the amount of sugar in their blood.

Mental illness

According to a study published by the World Health Organization (WHO) in 2001, mental-health problems are the main cause of disability and illness in the developed world. There are many different mental illnesses, which are grouped under broad categories, for example, anxiety disorders such as post-traumatic stress disorder, cognitive disorders such as amnesia, eating disorders such as anorexia nervosa, and substance-related disorders such as alcoholism.

Mental illnesses have a range of causes. Some are due to a chemical imbalances in the brain and can be treated with drugs. However, not all mental illness has a physical cause. Events in a person's life, such as the grief of losing a relative or stress at work, may result in mental-health problems. Symptoms of mental illness include depression, lethargy, and mood swings. In addition to medical supervision, people suffering from mental illnesses can often be helped with specialist counseling.

See also: AIDS • ANTIBIOTIC • BACTERIA • FUNGI KINGDOM • GENETICS • IMMUNE SYSTEM • LYMPHATIC SYSTEM • MEDICAL TECHNOLOGY • VACCINATION • VIRUS, BIOLOGICAL

Distillation

Distillation is a common process used in the laboratory and in industry to separate and purify liquids. It is used, for example, in oil refineries to turn crude oil into useful fuels, in making spirits such as brandy and whisky, and in purifying drinking water.

When water is heated to a temperature of 212°F (100°C), it starts to boil. The water changes into a gas, or vapor, which escapes into the air. This process is called vaporization. When the hot water vapor comes against a cold surface, it is cooled below its boiling point, and the vapor changes back into liquid water. This process is called condensation. Distillation includes the processes of vaporization and condensation. It involves heating up a liquid until it boils and then condensing the vapor that forms back into liquid.

The history of distillation

The ancient Greeks were the first people to use the process of distillation about two thousand years ago. It also became very important to the work of the early chemists, or alchemists, who followed soon after. Their tests and equipment laid the foundations for modern chemistry. The alchemists dreamed of turning common metals, such as lead, into gold by constant purification—removing unwanted chemicals and dirt from the molten metal. In distillation, heat is used to vaporize a mixture of liquids. As the vapors cool, the different parts of the mixture condense back into liquids. Since the vapors condense at different temperatures, the distillation process splits the mixture back into separate parts.

▶ *Distillation is used to separate useful liquids from crude (unrefined) oil at this oil refinery. Distillation is used in many other chemical industries.*

Distillation was the method of purification alchemists had been seeking. However, they had to devise their own equipment, so they adapted some of the apparatus used by glassworkers, goldsmiths, and others. The result, which emerged in the Middle Ages, was called a still.

The medieval still was made up of four parts—a furnace, a flask, a still head, and a collecting vessel. The furnace was the base of the equipment and burned wood or charcoal. The flask, which was then called a cucurbit, was made of pottery. The still head, called by the Greek name *ambix*, was a dome of metal or pottery with one or more spouts. It fit tightly over the flask. Since the spouts were cooler than the rest of the ambix, the gases produced by heating began to condense as soon as it reached them. The collecting vessel was a pottery flask with a narrow neck.

▲ *These copper stills from a distillery in France are used to make a liquor called cognac. All liquors are produced by distillation. The process concentrates the alcohol produced in the initial fermentation process.*

The medieval still has become a symbol of the European alchemists. No one is really sure what the alchemists were distilling, because they kept their work as secret as possible by writing about it in codes and strange languages. However, it is known that Arab scholar Abu ibn Bahr al-Basri al-Jahiz (776–868 CE) was distilling vinegar to make acetic acid in the year 800 CE.

By about 1150, alcohol was being distilled from wine to make liqueurs. This mostly took place in monasteries, and many liqueurs are still produced by monks. About the same time, alchemists were making alcohol for other purposes from the distillation of wine and a solution of quicklime.

The production of nitric acid (HNO_3) was first written about in 1300. This is a distillation of a solution of sodium nitrate ($NaNO_3$) and ferrous sulfate ($FeSO_4$). Nitric acid is an extremely important compound used to make nitrates, dyes, and explosives.

Simple distillation

Distillation can be used to purify water that is unfit for drinking, such as seawater. Seawater is undrinkable because it contains dissolved salts. When the sea water is boiled, only water vapor comes off. This can then be condensed into pure liquid water. The salts remain behind. This desalting process, called desalination, is used to provide drinking water in many desert countries.

Simple distillation can also be used to help separate a mixture of two liquids, as long as their boiling points are far enough apart. When the mixture is heated, the most volatile liquid (the one with the lowest boiling point) vaporizes first and can be collected separately.

In the laboratory, simple distillation is carried out by heating the liquid mixture in a flask and cooling the vapor with a Liebig condenser. This condenser is a glass tube surrounded by a jacket through which cold water flows. The condensed liquid, called the distillate, is collected in another flask.

Fractional distillation

Simple distillation is of limited use for separating a mixture of liquids whose boiling points are close together. For example, ordinary alcohol (boiling point 172°F or 78°C) and water (boiling point 212°F or 100°C) cannot be separated by simple distillation. Even at a temperature of 172°F (78°C), some water evaporates along with the alcohol. The distillate will therefore still contain water, though much less than before.

A better way of separating such mixtures is by fractional distillation (fractionation). In this process, the vapor passes up through a column packed with glass beads before entering the condenser. The temperature varies up through the column, becoming lower the higher up the column.

When the liquid mixture boils, its vapor rises up through the column. As it rises, it cools and starts to condense. The vapor of the least volatile (highest boiling point) liquid tends to condense first. This means that more of the most volatile vapor remains. This process happens all the way up the distillation column and results in a vapor rich in the most volatile fraction.

See also: CHEMISTRY • GAS • LIQUID • OIL EXPLORATION AND REFINING

Diving

Diving can be both an exciting sport and a dangerous occupation. Deep-sea divers brave many hazards to explore and work in the murky ocean depths. The demand for their service is ever increasing as people extend their search for mineral wealth from the land to the bottom of the sea.

People were diving underwater thousands of years ago in search of such valuable objects such as pearl oysters, sponges, and sunken treasure. However, they could remain submerged for only a few minutes before they had to come up for air. Then, around 300 BCE, Greek philosopher Aristotle (384–322 BCE) first described a device that allowed people to breathe underwater. It resembled an upturned bucket that trapped air inside when it was lowered into the water. Aristotle's invention was a primitive diving bell. Over the years, the diving bell became larger, so eventually the divers could sit inside it. In the 1700s, air pumps were developed to pump air down to the diving bells. Divers could therefore stay underwater for longer.

The diving suit

In the 1820s, German inventor Augustus Siebe (1788–1872) designed a diving helmet that could be supplied with air. It was a kind of personal diving bell, which allowed divers much more freedom in the water. From this developed a deep-sea diving

▼ *A scuba diver investigates a large piece of coral on an offshore reef. Scuba diving is undertaken by ocean scientists, marine engineers, and archaeologists, and it is also a popular leisure pursuit.*

suit that is still used today—the helmet suit. The body of the helmet suit is made of rubberized fabric and has a metal breastplate. A metal helmet clamps onto the breastplate. The helmet has glass portholes that enable the diver to see in all directions. It is supplied with compressed air from the surface through an air hose. The air is supplied at the same pressure as the water surrounding the diver. The air inside the diver's suit makes the diver light and buoyant. Lead boots and heavy weights attached to the front and back of the suit weigh the diver down so that he or she can walk on the seabed.

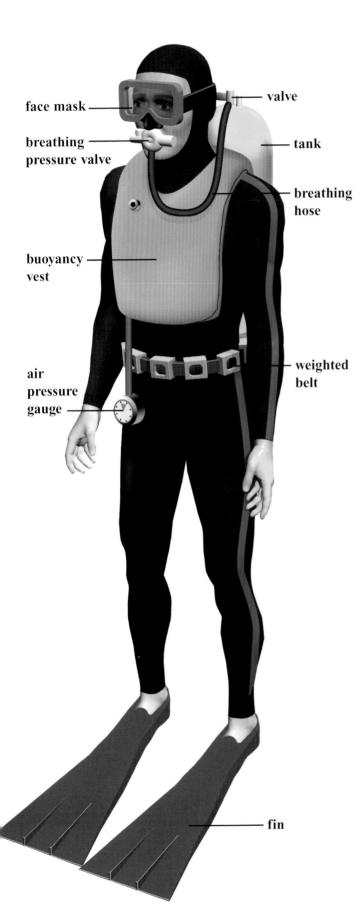

face mask

breathing pressure valve

buoyancy vest

air pressure gauge

valve

tank

breathing hose

weighted belt

fin

◀ *This illustration shows a fully equipped scuba diver ready to dive. The weighted belt and buoyancy vest are used to control the diver's depth. The air pressure gauge tells the diver how much air is left in the tank.*

▼ *Jacques-Yves Cousteau developed the aqualung in 1943. He was an avid oceanographer and explorer and made many underwater movies.*

▶ *The most important part of a diver's equipment is the demand valve. This device controls the air supply in the cylinders carried on the diver's back. It ensures that the air is supplied at the same pressure as the surrounding water.*

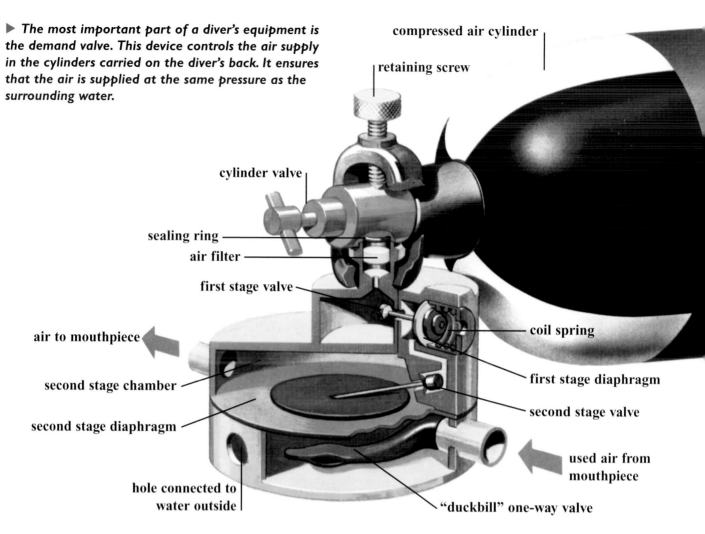

compressed air cylinder

retaining screw

cylinder valve

sealing ring

air filter

first stage valve

air to mouthpiece

coil spring

second stage chamber

first stage diaphragm

second stage diaphragm

second stage valve

used air from mouthpiece

hole connected to water outside

"duckbill" one-way valve

Scuba diving

Traditional diving suits are very cumbersome, and most divers now use scuba equipment for diving in shallow waters. Scuba stands for "self-contained underwater breathing apparatus." Scuba divers use an aqualung to breathe. This device was developed in 1943 by French underwater expert Jacques-Yves Cousteau (1910–1997).

Many people had tried to design an underwater breathing device, but none of them had understood that the air a diver breathed had to be at the same pressure as the surrounding water. Near the surface, water pressure is much the same as the pressure of the air people normally breathe. However, the water pressure increases with increasing depth. In the ocean depths, the water is pushing so hard on the body that it is difficult for the diver to expand his or her lungs to breathe properly. The pressures inside and outside the lungs are not the same.

What divers need is some device for supplying them with air at exactly the same pressure as the pressure of the water surrounding them. In that way, the air pressure inside and outside the lungs will be the same, and the diver will be able to breathe without any effort.

The aqualung, commonly called a scuba unit, has three main parts. First, there is a cylinder (or sometimes two) with a harness so the diver can attach it to his or her back. The cylinder contains the diver's air supply, pumped into the cylinder under a pressure of about 3,000 pounds per square inch (psi). The cylinder has a pressure gauge so that the diver knows exactly how much air is left. Second, the diver has a mouthpiece connected to the cylinder by two flexible tubes—the diver's lifeline to the air supply. Third, the diver has the most important piece of equipment of all—the demand valve, which regulates the air supply to the diver.

▶ *A diver uses his knife to cut away thick fishing lines snagged on a ship's propeller. Divers carry out all sorts of important marine maintenance work.*

How the demand valve works

A simple demand valve is a box with a flexible diaphragm dividing it in two. One half is open to the surrounding water. The other half has an inlet from the cylinder and an outlet to the mouthpiece. The inlet from the cylinder is controlled by a valve that can be turned on and off by the diaphragm.

When the pressure of the surrounding water is more than the air pressure in the demand valve, the diaphragm is pushed by the water and the air valve is opened. Pressurized air comes into the air chamber and pushes the diaphragm back against the water pressure until the air pressure and the water pressure are equal. The returning movement of the diaphragm closes the valve again, and the air is cut off. This mechanism ensures that the diver always gets a supply of air at the same pressure as the surrounding water.

This simple type of demand valve is called a single-stage valve. It works well enough in shallow waters, but the pressure at the depths of the ocean is too much. Deeper dives require a two-stage valve.

In the first stage, the air pressure is reduced from the very high pressure of the cylinder to about 100 pounds per square inch above the pressure of the water. In the second stage, this pressure is reduced to water pressure by a valve that is similar to the simple single-stage demand valve.

Using the scuba

Divers using an aqualung can stay underwater as long as there is air in the cylinders. Dive times are long enough for the aqualung to be useful for divers conducting underwater archaeology, salvage, and rescue operations. In warm waters, scuba divers need not wear diving suits, but in cool waters suits must be worn to retain body heat. Otherwise body temperature might be dangerously lowered, causing hypothermia, which could soon make the diver unconscious. Diving suits are usually made from an artificial foamlike rubber called neoprene.

Drysuits are watertight and have seals at the neck and wrists. More common, however, is the wetsuit, which is not watertight. It traps a thin layer of water between the wetsuit and the body. The diver's body heat warms this water, which then acts as an insulating layer to keep the diver's body warm.

Modern deep-sea diving

For deep-sea diving work, scuba equipment is not good. The pressure in deep water is very high, and air must be supplied to the diver at the same high pressure. The air in a cylinder would last for a few minutes in these conditions, so it must be supplied to the diver through a tube from an external supply. This supply is usually contained in a diving bell.

In fact, the breathing mixture supplied for deep-sea diving is not the air people normally breathe. Normal air is primarily a mixture of nitrogen and

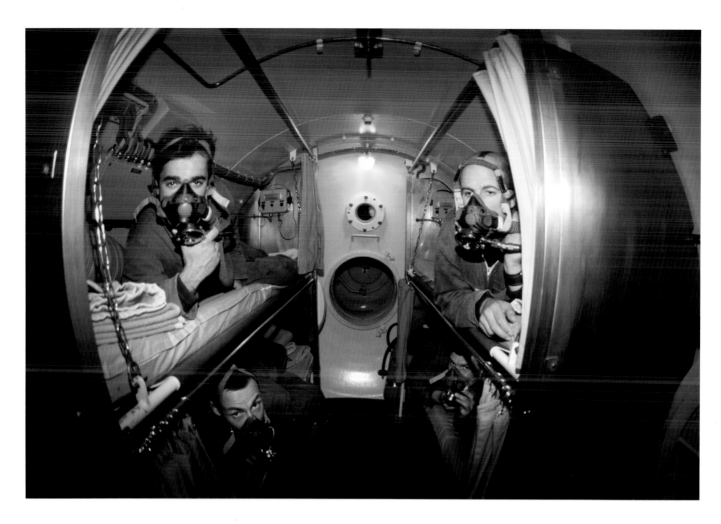

▲ *These deep-sea saturation divers are sitting in a decompression chamber. When divers work at extreme depths, it can take them up to a week to recover fully. The divers have to return to the surface of the ocean in pressurized diving bells.*

oxygen, plus a tiny amount of a few other gases. Normal air cannot be used for deep diving because nitrogen at high pressure affects the diver's brain, making him or her feel intoxicated. For deep-sea dives, the diver breathes a mixture of oxygen and helium. This mixture does not affect the diver's brain, but the helium in it gives the diver's voice a characteristic high-pitched squeak.

The bends

Divers working in very deep water face another major problem. At high pressure, more gas dissolves in the bloodstream. This is not a problem when the diver remains underwater. When the pressure is reduced, however, the dissolved gas comes back out of the bloodstream. If the pressure change is sudden, the gas will form bubbles in the body tissues. The diver will experience severe cramps and double up in pain. This condition is called decompression sickness, or "the bends." In extreme cases it can be fatal.

To prevent the bends, the pressure on the diver's body must be reduced gradually in a process called decompression. This can be done by allowing the diver to resurface slowly, ascending in a series of steps and pauses at certain depths.

This step-by-step ascent is very time consuming, however. Scuba divers can descend to depths of about 160 feet (50 meters) directly from the surface. From this depth, it can take a diver up to three hours to decompress. For deeper dives, the decompression time is even longer. A deep-sea diver working at a depth of 400 feet (120 meters) for an hour needs 15 hours of decompression time. For deep-sea dives, pressurized diving bells are

▶ *A deep-sea diver in a Jim suit. This particular suit has thruster propellers to help the diver to move around in the heavy suit. Because the diver is at atmospheric pressure inside the suit, there is no need to decompress.*

often used to bring the divers back up to the surface. The divers are then transferred to a decompression chamber. The pressure in the chamber is slowly lowered to normal atmospheric pressure, and the divers can then come out safely.

Saturation diving

In offshore oil fields, commercial divers can work at depths of 1,000 feet (about 300 meters) or more. From such depths, the decompression time can be a matter of days. It is not practical for the divers to decompress after each dive.

Instead, saturation divers are kept under pressure between dives. After a dive, the divers are taken back to a decompression chamber in a pressurized diving bell or submersible. They live in the chamber, which is kept at high pressure, until the next dive. They can work like this for a week or more, during which time their bodies become saturated with gas. When the series of deep-sea dives is complete, these saturation divers take up to a week to decompress.

Atmospheric diving

There is an alternative to diving under pressure. Some diving suits are strong enough to withstand the very high water pressures at depths of several hundred feet. They are called atmospheric diving suits because the diver is able to breathe air at ordinary atmospheric pressure. Consequently, the diver does not run the risk of developing decompression sickness.

In the 1920s, British inventor Joseph Peress (1896–1978) came up with the idea of making a ball-and-socket joint for an atmospheric suit. This joint was designed to work on the same principle as our own hip joints. This development led to the best-known modern atmospheric suit, called the Jim suit. The Jim suit was named for Peress's assistant, Jim Jarratt, who made many test dives in the suit. Jim suits can work at depths of more than 1,640 feet (500 meters). The diver is supplied with oxygen through a rebreather, which is a device that uses chemicals to convert the carbon dioxide (CO_2) exhaled by a diver back into oxygen. The diver can talk to people at the surface through an umbilical communication line.

The latest atmospheric Jim suits are made from extremely lightweight composite materials. They often have gripper "hands," which are operated by the diver's hands inside. Some have electric-powered propellers attached to allow the diver to move about with ease.

See also: AIR • OCEAN • OXYGEN • PRESSURE • SUBMERSIBLE

DNA

Complex molecules of DNA, or deoxyribonucleic acid, are found inside the cells of all living organisms, from mushrooms and trees to fleas and elephants. DNA is the building block of life. It carries a code, in the form of genes, that acts as the blueprint for organizing each organism's body.

DNA is a complex chemical called a polymer. Like other polymers, DNA consists of a chain that is formed from several smaller units. Unlike most polymers, however, DNA chains also bond together in pairs. These paired chains look rather like a ladder that has been twisted around on itself. Biologists call this structure a double helix.

Carrying the code

Organisms store DNA inside cells. Simple organisms, such as bacteria, have a single loop of DNA. More complex organisms, such as humans, have much longer pieces of DNA. The DNA of most organisms is coiled up into structures called chromosomes, which are stored inside the nucleus of the cell. If one took all the DNA from every cell in a single person's body and laid it out end to end, the strands would stretch from Earth to the Moon about six thousand times.

Strands of DNA contain specific sections called genes mixed with regions that have no known function. Genes are the units of heredity and contain the code for a single characteristic. For

▼ *A scientist prepares DNA for analysis. DNA studies have revealed much about the evolution of different organisms and the ways in which they are related.*

452

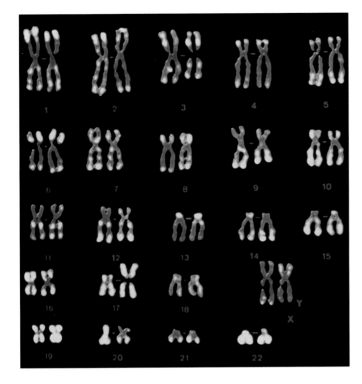

◄ *The DNA in almost all cells groups together into structures called chromosomes. Human cell nuclei contain 23 pairs of chromosomes.*

sugar-phosphate backbone

► *The DNA double helix looks rather like a twisted ladder. The sides of the ladder consist of a backbone of deoxyribose sugars linked by phosphate groups. Base pairs form the rungs of the ladder. Adenine pairs with thymine, and cytosine pairs with guanine.*

cytosine

adenine

guanine

thymine

example, some people have the gene for blonde hair or green eyes. Parents pass on at least some of these genes to their offspring.

DNA structure

A DNA polymer is an intricate combination of six separate units. Deoxyribose sugar is the main unit. It forms the sides of the molecule's twisted ladder structure. The next units are ringed molecules called nucleic acids, or bases. DNA contains four bases called adenine, cytosine, guanine, and thymine. One end of each base forms a bond with the deoxyribose sugar, and the other end forms a bond with another base from the second DNA chain. The bonded bases, therefore, form the rungs of the ladder. To complete the long double helix, the deoxyribose sugars must link together. The links in the chain are called phosphates, the sixth and final part of the DNA molecule.

Base pairing

The bases that link the two chains of the DNA ladder bond in a specific way. The largest of the two bases are adenine and guanine. These chemicals belong to a class of compounds called purines. The smaller pair, cytosine and thymine, belong to a class

of compounds known as pyrimidines. Every rung of the DNA ladder is made up of one purine bonded to one pyrimidine. Adenine (A) pairs with thymine (T), and cytosine (C) always pairs with guanine (G). The sequence of bases along the chain of DNA therefore forms a simple four-letter alphabet A, C, G, and T. This base sequence forms the code that makes up the genes. Body cells use this genetic code to make the material they need to survive and reproduce.

Decoding genes

Living bodies manufacture many different proteins, and they are used for many different jobs. Some are needed for muscle growth; others are needed for the skin. However, the most crucial function of

▶ *Maurice Wilkins studied the structure of DNA using a technique called X-ray diffraction. The X-ray patterns he obtained showed that the double helix model of DNA suggested by Crick and Watson was correct.*

proteins is as enzymes. Enzymes control all life processes, from digesting food to releasing the energy needed to move. The genes in DNA contain a code—in the form of specific sequences of base pairs—that the body uses to make proteins.

Transcription and translation

Proteins are complex polymers made up of chains of smaller chemicals called amino acids. In most living organisms, proteins are made of just 20 amino acids. The exact order of amino acids determines what shape the completed protein will take and what job it will do.

When a cell needs to make proteins, the double strands of DNA unzip inside the nucleus. Enzymes then read the DNA code and use it to make a chemical called ribonucleic acid, or RNA. This process is called transcription. RNA is very similar to DNA, but it consists of a single chain of ribose sugars instead of the double chain of deoxyribose

sugars of DNA. One of the bases is also different. RNA contains no thymine—the other pyrimidine is uracil. The RNA chain, called messenger RNA (mRNA), then leaves the nucleus and is processed by another structure in the cell, called a ribosome. Ribosomes are the cell's protein factories, reading the mRNA and turning it into useful proteins. This process is called translation.

The genetic code

To make proteins, the sequence of DNA bases is broken down into three-letter code "words" called codons. Each codon contains a combination of A, C, G, or T, depending on the order of the bases in the chain. The DNA code contains 64 codons; 61 of these specify the 20 different amino acids. This is many more codons than are needed, but some amino acids may be specified by more than one codon. The last three codons are "stop signs." They tell the ribosome to stop making amino acids, which signals the end of the protein chain.

DID YOU KNOW?

The structure of DNA was unraveled by English scientist Francis Crick (1916–2004) and U.S. biologist James Watson (1928–) in 1953. Crick and Watson used patterns formed by X-rays of DNA molecules made by New Zealand–born British physicist Maurice Wilkins (1916–2004) and his assistant Rosalind Franklin (1920–1958) to figure out how the base pairs joined. Crick and Watson put forward the double helix model of DNA, and the X-ray patterns confirmed this. Understanding DNA has not only explained how life on Earth works, it also has allowed people to control DNA and the way organisms develop. This process, called genetic engineering, has proved to be extremely useful in science.

The codons in the DNA sequence are transcribed onto the long mRNA chain. As the mRNA moves through the ribosome, molecules of transfer RNA (tRNA) gather along the mRNA chain. The molecules of tRNA do not form chains. They consist of just three bases. The three tRNA bases form an "anticodon," which bonds with the mRNA transcribed from the DNA codon. As well as bases, tRNA molecules also carry a single amino acid. This amino acid is the one encoded in the mRNA and the DNA before that. The tRNA molecules lock onto the corresponding part of the mRNA, and this lines all the amino acids up in the correct order. The amino acids then break off from the tRNA and join to form a complete protein.

DNA mutations

The instructions of life encoded in DNA can be copied and passed on from cell to cell and then from parents to children. Mistakes made during the copying process are called mutations. Mutations can also arise through environmental factors, such as cigarette smoke or ultraviolet light from the Sun. Most mutations are a disaster. An example is the crippling blood disorder sickle-cell anemia, which arises when one base in the DNA sequence is substituted for another. Sickle-cell anemia makes red blood cells collapse into a sickle shape.

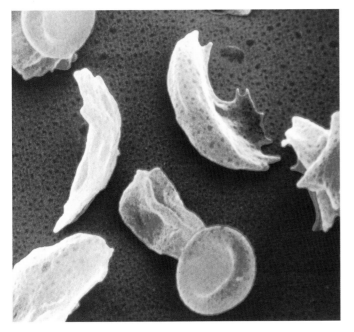

DID YOU KNOW?

The silicon chips that control personal computers have got faster and smaller since the first ones were invented around 50 years ago. However, there is a limit to how fast silicon chips can work. Some scientists think that the computers of the future will use DNA biochips to do the job of silicon chips. Biochips will combine DNA molecules into circuits that are far smaller and faster than the latest silicon chips. Simple DNA computers have already been made, but it will be a very long time before engineers can construct biochips intricate enough to rival the most powerful microprocessors in use today.

A few mutations turn out to produce genes that are even better than what was there before. These random beneficial changes in DNA are essential to the process of evolution. Evolution is the genetic change that takes place over time within a group of organisms. Through DNA mutations, organisms can develop new characteristics. Over time, new kinds of organisms can rise.

DNA fingerprinting

Since DNA is unique to everyone, it can be used by the police to identify people. Criminals often leave skin, hairs, and other traces of body tissues or fluids at a crime scene. All these things contain DNA. Using a complex separation technique, police can compare the DNA "fingerprint" found at the crime scene with the genes of their suspect. If the two DNA profiles match, the police can place their suspect at the crime scene.

◄ *This picture shows the characteristic sickle-shaped red blood cells associated with sickle-cell anemia. This inherited blood disorder is caused by a DNA mutation.*

See also: CRICK, FRANCIS, AND JAMES WATSON • GENETICS • PROTEIN

Doppler effect

The change in sound that someone hears when a moving object speeds past them is an example of the Doppler effect. This effect also occurs with other waves, such as light and radio waves, when the source of the wave is moving relative to the observer.

Most people have heard the way the sound of an ambulance siren seems to drop in pitch as it speeds past. The siren makes a high-pitched sound as the ambulance draws closer, but the pitch drops as soon as it passes by. The sound appears to change from a high note to a low note, even though the siren is making exactly the same sound all the time. Austrian physicist Christian Johann Doppler (1803–1853) first investigated this effect in 1842.

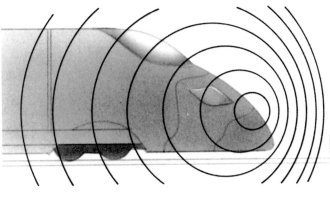

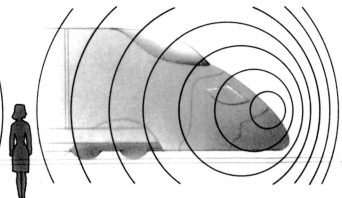

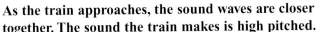

As the train approaches, the sound waves are closer together. The sound the train makes is high pitched.

As the train moves away, the sound waves are farther apart. The sound the train makes is low pitched.

▲ *The distance between the crest of each sound wave determines the pitch of the sound. The sound waves in front of the moving train are closer together, so the listener hears a high-pitched sound. The sound waves behind the train are farther apart, so the listener hears a lower-pitched sound.*

◄ *Airplane pilots rely on Doppler radar devices to navigate and keep a safe distance from other aircraft. As the airplane moves through the air, the Doppler devices measure the airplane's distance from the ground and from other aircraft.*

Changing wavelength

Sound travels through the air in waves. The pitch of a sound depends on the wavelength—the distance between the crests of each sound wave. The greater the distance between the crests, the lower the pitch of the sound. When an ambulance speeds toward a person, siren blaring, the wavelength appears to be shorter. The person hears a high-pitched sound. As the ambulance moves away, the wavelength appears to be longer. The person hears a lower-pitched sound.

Redshift and blueshift

Light also travels through the air in waves, so an apparent change in wavelength occurs when the source of the light is moving. Astronomers have found that the light a star emits is sometimes more blue or more red than it should be. Visible light consists of seven different colors, each with a different wavelength. Blue light has a shorter wavelength than red light. If the light a star emits is more blue than it should be, the Doppler effect tells us that the star must be moving toward Earth. This blueshift is similar to the shortening of sound waves when an ambulance draws closer. If the light is more red than it should be, astronomers know that the star is moving away from Earth. This change is called a redshift. Most stars have redshifts, so they are moving away from Earth, which indicates that the universe is expanding.

See also: ASTRONOMY • RADAR • SOUND

Drill

Most drills have a hard cutter, called a bit, that rotates rapidly and bores a hole through the material. Other drills have bits that chip the material away with a hammering action. Laser drills burn holes in materials using powerful beams of laser light. Some laser beams can even cut through diamond, which is the hardest substance on Earth.

Drills have been used for centuries by doctors, dentists, and craftspeople. The first drills were probably simple hand tools for piercing holes in soft materials such as wood. Over the years, drill design has improved in three main ways. Harder metals were used to make the cutting bits, and the design of the bits gradually improved. Later, the drill itself became a machine powered by an electric motor and air turbines.

Dental drills

The dental drill is an example of a simple hand tool that developed into a precision power tool. Dentists use drills to remove infected and decayed parts of the teeth. The hole formed is then filled with a soft material, called amalgam, that hardens quickly.

One tool used by early dentists was a round file. It had a thin, round handle, which could be twisted using the thumb and fingers, making it a simple form of drill. This tool soon became blunt, so drills with replaceable bits were developed. By the middle of the nineteenth century, one type of dental drill had a bit mounted at the end of a long, flexible shaft. This design made it easy for the dentist to drill teeth from almost any angle. Then various kinds of mechanisms were designed to make it easier to turn the bit by hand.

The first foot-operated dental drill was made in 1872. To use the drill, the dentist pushed a plate with his or her foot, and this turned a drill bit

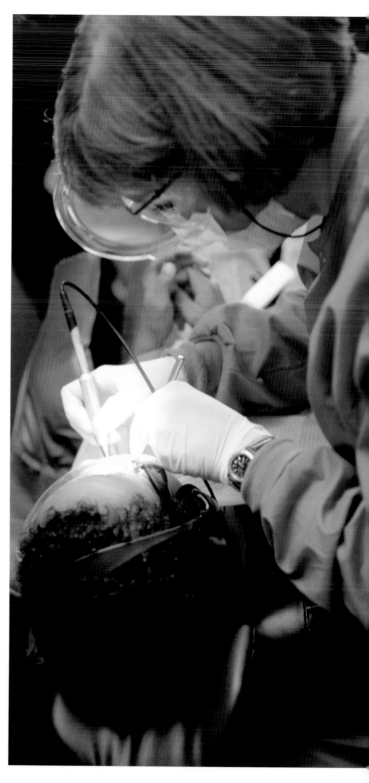

▲ A dentist uses an air drill to remove the decayed parts of her patient's tooth. Air drills work at higher speeds and are much easier to use than drills containing electric motors.

▶ *This woman is using a cordless electric drill to attach some light fixtures to a wall. Many households have drills for simple maintenance and home improvements.*

mounted at the end of a long, movable arm. By the end of the nineteenth century, electric motors were often used to power dental drills.

In the latest air-turbine dental drills, compressed air is fed along a hose to a handpiece, where the air blows a rotor around at high speed. The rotor turns the bit at up to 800,000 revolutions per minute. The high speed of the rotating bit means that the drilling is smoother and therefore much more comfortable for the patient.

Electric drills

The electric drill is a portable drilling machine powered by an electric motor. The drill is usually shaped like a pistol, with a hand grip and a switch operated like a trigger.

For safety, a trigger lock is often provided. This lock keeps the trigger in the "on" position, so that the operator does not have to keep pressing the trigger. On some models, the trigger acts as a speed control. At high speeds, the high friction between the object being drilled and the bit would cause the bit to overheat and it would quickly become soft and blunt. By applying only a little pressure on the trigger, the operator can make the drill turn slowly.

Larger, heavier models have an extra handle fixed to the side of the drill body so that both hands can safely be used to steady the drill and press it onto the work surface with an even pressure.

Principles of operation

The electric motor in the drill produces a high torque (turning power) at low speeds. Suppose, for example, that the bit starts to jam in the hole it is cutting. This will force the motor to slow down, but the torque will increase. The extra power produced will usually ensure that the bit keeps turning.

In some electric drills, the bit holder, called the chuck, is driven directly by the motor. Since this arrangement gives a very high bit speed, in most drills the speed is reduced by means of gears. These couple the motor to the chuck, giving a maximum

bit speed of about 2,500 revolutions per minute. The chuck has three jaws and protrudes from the front of the drill. A sleeve around the chuck is turned to open or close the jaws that hold the bit. In some drills, final tightening of the jaws is carried out using a special key to turn the collar. Different bits are available for drilling brick, metals, wood, and other materials.

Laser drilling

The most advanced drills are laser drills. Although they are called drills, they do not work in the same way as conventional drills. Rather than using the friction of a rotating bit to make holes in materials, they use powerful laser light to vaporize the material.

Laser drills can be used on almost all materials, including metals and alloys, ceramics, polymers, and composite materials. They are highly accurate and can drill whatever shape of hole is desired. They can also drill much smaller holes than conventional drills, often as little as $\frac{1}{10,000}$ inch (0.00025 centimeter) in diameter.

See also: BEARING • DENTISTRY • LASER

Drilling rig

A drilling rig is used for drilling oil wells both on land and at sea. The well can be 5 miles (8 kilometers) deep, and the drill that passes through the hole may weigh several hundred tons.

The first well to produce oil was drilled in Pennsylvania in 1859. Since then, millions of bore holes have been sunk worldwide, although only a few of these have yielded decent amounts of oil. Before an oil well is drilled, geologists study the region to figure out the most likely location of oil. Drilling is an expensive operation, so the number of bore holes drilled must be kept to a minimum.

Most of the world's oil wells have been drilled on land. Now that most of the likely land supplies have been exhausted, offshore oil drilling has steadily become much more common. Oil rigs at sea are more expensive to build than those on land, but both work in the same basic way.

Drill string and bit

To sink a bore hole, a rotating drill bit (a cutting tool) with hard, toothed, revolving wheels is lowered into the ground. In the hardest rock, diamond or tungsten carbide (WC) teeth are used. It may take an hour to drill 1 inch (2.5 centimeters). In softer rock, rates of about 100 yards (90 meters) per hour are possible.

The bit is fixed to the end of a series of drill pipes, called a drill string. Each pipe is around 30 feet (9 meters) long and about 4½ to 5½ inches (11 to 14 centimeters) across. The pipes just above the drill bit are heavier than the rest and are called drill collars. They put enough weight onto the bit to force it into the ground.

As the drill bit bores further down into the ground, more drill pipes are screwed onto the end of the drill string. By the time the drill string is a few miles long, it weighs several hundred tons.

▲ *Oil workers add another pipe to the drill string on an offshore oil rig.*

Most of this weight is supported by the rig on the surface; otherwise, the string would be compressed under its own weight and would tend to break or jam in the hole.

Drilling operations

The most noticeable part of the drilling rig is the derrick (drilling tower). This steel structure may be up to 200 feet (60 meters) high. It is used to hoist

▶ *A tug tows an oil rig into place. Once on site, the rig will be anchored with huge steel cables. Depending on the size of the underwater oil reserves, the rig can drill on the same site for many years.*

and stack lengths of drill pipe and to support the drill string. At the base of the derrick is a rotating table driven by a powerful motor. The table turns at about 120 revolutions per minute. It has a central hole, through which a square or six-sided pipe called a kelly can slide. The kelly hangs from the top of the derrick and forms the top section of the drill string. As the table rotates, it turns the kelly and, hence, the rest of the drill string and the bit. As the bit drills into the ground, the kelly slides down the hole in the table.

When the top of the kelly has nearly reached the table, drilling stops. The drill string is then wedged in place, and the kelly is disconnected. Another length of ordinary drill pipe is screwed onto the string, and the kelly is replaced on top. Drilling can then begin again.

In drilling a typical well, this task must be repeated hundreds of times. Whenever the bit becomes blunt, the entire string has to be removed so that a new bit can be put in. Then the string has to be connected again. To speed up this operation, the drill string is unscrewed in three-pipe sections, instead of being completely dismantled. However, the whole job can take about a day, depending on the length of the string. The new bit may also be blunted after only a few hours of drilling if the ground contains hard rock.

During drilling, a chemical "mud" is pumped down the drill pipes and forced through a jet in the drill bit. It then passes back up to the surface through the space between the pipe and the hole that has been drilled. The mud cools the bit and also lubricates it, thus reducing friction and heat. The mud also carries the drilled-out material to the surface, prevents the hole from caving in, and helps control any flow of oil or gas from the well.

Gas and oil are often found together, and sometimes they occur in pockets at high pressure. Before mud was used, high-pressure oil or gas was liable to shoot out suddenly to the surface. With mud filling the hole, the pressure is rarely enough for the oil or gas to force its way to the top. When traces of oil are found in the mud returning to the surface, it is tested for quality. If the flow rate proves to be sufficient, tubing is inserted in the hole and extraction begins.

Offshore drilling

Various types of rigs are used when searching for oil at sea. Converted ships or fixed platforms can be used in shallow water. At greater depths, up to about 300 feet (90 meters), a platform with extending legs is first towed into position. Then the legs are lowered onto the seabed. Semisubmersible rigs have floats below the surface supporting a platform above, clear of the waves.

Once an oil deposit has been located, a well is drilled using a fully equipped production platform, a huge steel or concrete structure that stands on the seabed. Up to 30 wells can be drilled from one platform by altering the direction of drilling. After treatment to remove gas and water, the oil is brought ashore by pipeline or by tanker.

See also: DRILL • GEOLOGY • OIL EXPLORATION AND REFINING • PIPELINE • TANKER

Drug industry

The drug industry produces a wide range of substances, collectively called drugs, to treat many different illnesses. Some common drugs, such as aspirin, can be bought by adults over the counter in a drugstore. Other drugs are very powerful and can only be prescribed by a physician.

People in ancient times used plants and parts of animals as drugs, but the treatments were rarely scientifically proved to be of any use. However, ancient people are responsible for introducing ideas that form the basis of much of modern medicine. For example, the Chinese used iron-rich liver to cure anemia, and the Greeks and Romans took opium to relieve pain.

◀ *Greek physician Galen of Pergamum (129–c. 216 CE) influenced medicine and the treatment of disease for centuries after his death.*

Drug production in the United States can be traced back to the American War of Independence (1775–1783), when the army's chief pharmacist Andrew Craigie (1754–1819) set up a laboratory in Carlisle, Pennsylvania, to supply drugs to the army. When the war was over, Craigie continued to make drugs, and other pharmacists in the area set up their own businesses. In the United States, Pennsylvania remains a leader in drug production, followed closely by New York and New Jersey.

Modern drugs

Most drugs are huge molecules that consist of thousands of atoms strung together and folded into complex shapes. A drug works if its shape fits some other important site in the body. For example, a virus may enter a cell by attaching to a part of the cell membrane called a receptor. If a drug molecule is shaped so that it fits that receptor, it will block it and thus stop the virus from infecting the cell.

Modern drugs are very powerful and should be given to people only when they really need them. Therefore, the physician's diagnosis has to be accurate. The patient must also be careful to follow the course of the treatment according to the physician's instructions.

Most drugs usually have two names—an official international chemical name and a local trade or brand name. The same drug, made by different companies, may therefore be marketed under several different names in any one country and under a different set of names in another. In the United States, the naming of drugs is regulated by the Food and Drug Administration (FDA).

In the past, making up a prescription involved weighing and mixing many different chemicals. The instructions for some prescriptions ran to several pages. Most modern medicines are prepared and packaged by the manufacturer that researched

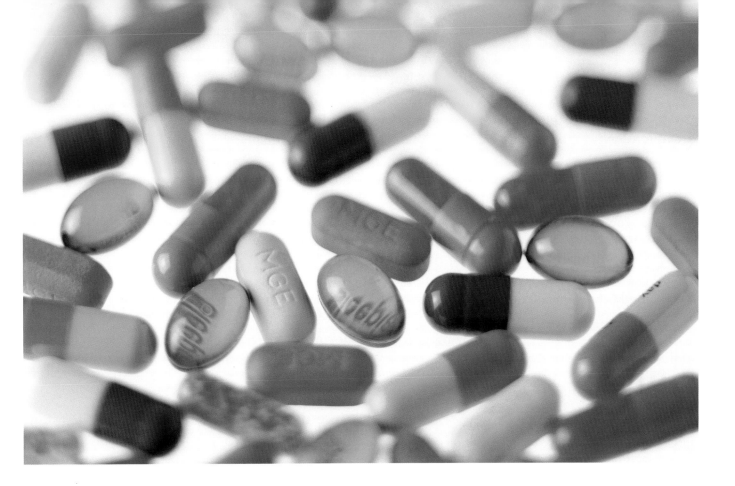

and marketed the drug. Drugs now come in many different dosage forms, including liquids, ointments, pills, powders, and tablets.

Side effects

Most people like to know what effect the drug their physician has prescribed will have on them. Drugs interfere with the body's natural way of working in some way. They are therefore "foreign" to the body, and perhaps even poisonous if taken in too large doses or too frequently. Drugs may also affect parts of the body other than the area they are supposed to affect. Some drugs, therefore, may cause unpleasant side effects.

Some side effects, such as nausea and mild fever, are minor complaints and can be tolerated. Others, such as allergies and blood disorders, may mean that the physician must stop prescribing the drug. One drug may also interact with another drug that the patient is taking for a different illness. Physicians must always be aware of this problem, because there are now so many drugs available for every medical problem. Many of these drugs are available over the counter.

▲ Modern drugs come in a range of dosage forms, such as these capsules and tablets. Advantages of solid dosages include greater stability, smaller bulk, accurate dosage, and ease of production.

Developing and testing drugs

A large part of the drug industry's huge income is spent on the research and development of new medicines. Scientists called medicinal chemists or pharmacologists develop and test new drugs before they go on sale to ensure they are both safe and effective. Developing a new drug is a long, complex process. Government safety laws and the company's own needs ensure that it can take nine or ten years before the drug can be sold to people. Research and development may cost tens of millions of dollars. It has been estimated that out of every 10,000 drugs worked on, usually only one reaches commercial production.

At the last stage of the testing procedure, the drug is given to people. At first, different patients will be given different doses to determine what dose is best and safest. If these tests show that the drug is safe and that it works, it will be compared with others already in use. Physicians will give the new drug to one group of patients, and another drug to another group, and compare the results.

Until recently, most drugs were developed by trial and error. Scientists tested thousands of chemicals and, once in a while, found one that could cure a disease. In the 1990s, they were designing new drugs to order. Scientists start with known drugs and create new molecules with similar shapes. The drugs they start from are called prototypes. Many prototypes come from plants. For example, the anesthetic cocaine is extracted from coca leaf. It is highly addictive, so doctors rarely give it to patients. Instead, they use the non-addictive synthetic drug xylocaine.

▼ *Animal testing is a controversial topic. The drug industry routinely uses animals to screen new drugs before they can be approved for human use. Some people would like to stop animal experimentation. They think that animals have rights, just like people do.*

Antibiotics (bacteria killers) are another kind of prototype. Natural antibiotics such as penicillin are made by microorganisms as a defense against other microorganisms. New antibiotics modeled on natural ones have saved millions of people from life-threatening bacterial infections.

Some modern drugs are based on chemicals called hormones. Hormones are produced by the endocrine glands. These glands secrete hormones into the bloodstream, and the hormones travel to different parts of the body, regulating body processes such as growth and metabolism. Physicians now use artificial drugs that resemble hormones to treat asthma, high blood pressure, mental illness, rheumatism, and even cancer.

Source in the sea

Since the 1950s, scientists have been discovering more potentially useful chemicals in organisms that live in the sea. For example, powerful painkillers

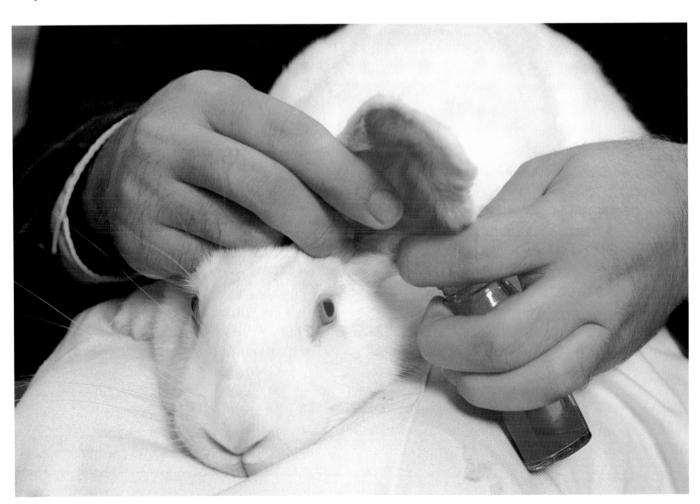

► *This picture shows "inhibition zones" resulting from a sensitivity test of 12 antibiotics. Red paper disks are soaked in an antibiotic solution and then placed in a petri dish containing a bacterial culture. The size of the inhibition zones (the clear areas around the disks) is a measure of the sensitivity of the bacteria to the antibiotics.*

and anti-inflammatory agents have been found in a sponge that lives in the western Pacific Ocean and in a soft coral from the Caribbean Sea. Both are in the long process of development by the drug industry. Oceans are also being explored as a source for new drugs to treat the many bacterial and viral diseases that plague people.

The placebo

Experiments show that some people think of drugs as something "magical." If they believe in the drugs they are taking, they will feel better. Even if these people are given a sugar pill instead of their drug, they will still feel better. This effect is often referred to as the placebo effect. Experiments on people who take sleeping tablets showed that if they were given dummy tablets, they still enjoyed a good night's sleep. Only when they were asked to do without any tablets did they stay awake.

Treating drugs sensibly

There are some medical complaints, such as influenza and the common cold, that cannot yet be cured by drugs. Other complaints, such as constipation, indigestion, and insomnia, can often be cured by changing habits, such as eating and sleeping, rather than by taking pills continually. It is unfortunate, but true, that people take more drugs than they normally need.

Licensing of pharmaceuticals

In 1937, a batch of an antibiotic called sulfanilamide became contaminated and more than one hundred people died. In response to this tragedy, the United States government set up careful procedures to ensure that all drugs are safe.

Every drug now sold in the United States must be licensed by the FDA. To receive a license, a new drug must undergo a series of strict tests—first on animals and then on people. Drug manufacturers must submit detailed information to the FDA. They must report on all the tests they have done on the new drug and describe how the drug is manufactured. Impurities may creep in during the manufacturing process, or they may even lurk in the additives used to give a tablet its color, shape, or flavor. The FDA insists that all side effects be reported. These side effects must be described in any information that the drug company sends to physicians about the drug.

Even with all this caution, there is still one problem drug manufacturers face. A new drug may have a side effect that appears only in a very small percentage of the population. In that case, the hazard might not show up until the drug has been prescribed to several hundred thousand patients. To guard against this problem, drug manufacturers have adopted a policy known as post-marketing surveillance. Every physician who prescribes the new drug will be asked to keep a close watch on his or her patients and report any new or unusual side effects to the drug manufacturer.

See also: AIDS • ALLERGY • ANESTHETIC • MEDICAL TECHNOLOGY • SURGERY

Dye and dyeing

Early humans decorated their bodies with paint, using different pigments from animals, plants, and substances found in the soil and rocks. Early attempts to color fabrics involved using these paints as dyes.

The first attempts at coloring textiles were often disappointing because the materials that made fine body paints did not always work as well on fabrics. Many of these early coloring materials were insoluble, which means they did not dissolve in water. As a result, they could not penetrate inside the fibers of the fabric. These materials were finely ground and mixed with fats or oils to form a kind of paint. When applied to cloth, this paint simply stuck to the surface of the fabric and, after a short time, it would flake off.

Of all the natural coloring materials available, only a few were suitable as dyes. The rest faded in sunlight, or else their color came out when the fabric was washed.

Synthetic dyes

Until the 1850s, only natural coloring materials were available as dyes. In 1851, English chemist William Perkin (1838–1907) introduced the first synthetic (artificial) dye.

This substance, called mauveine, was made from aniline (a product of coal tar). The new mauve dye was a great success, and scientists in many countries started to search for ways of making other synthetic dyes. They were very successful, and thousands of dyes were made from coal-tar ingredients such as aniline, anthracene, benzene, and toluene.

▶ *William Perkin was just 18 years old when he discovered the world's first synthetic dye, called mauveine. Realizing the commercial potential of his discovery, Perkin set up a factory producing the dye and became an extremely successful businessman.*

The first synthetic dyes were very popular because they were more brilliant than natural dyes. However, even though they worked well on animal fibers, such as silk and wool, they soon washed out of cotton or linen. This problem was overcome by using a process called mordanting. This process had been developed before synthetic dyes and was used to protect natural dyes against washing.

Mordanting involved treating fibers with chemicals called mordants—solutions of tannic acid and metal salts or, sometimes, the salts alone. When the fibers were later dyed, the mordants reacted with the dyes to form insoluble colored products, which became trapped inside tiny cavities in the fibers. Since the products of the reaction were insoluble, they could not be removed by washing. However, this did not mean that the material was permanently colored. Unfortunately, the early synthetic dyes tended to fade in sunlight. Much better dyes have since been developed.

▲ Yarn is dyed in a traditional vat in Oaxaca, Mexico. Dyeing is most effective at high temperatures, so the fabric is steeped in a dye solution that is heated to just below the boiling point.

Azo dyes

In 1858, a chemist called Peter Gries discovered a way of making synthetic dyes by joining together various organic compounds. Organic compounds are carbon-containing substances. They occur in almost all living organisms. A chemical reaction causes the molecules of the organic compounds to link together by forming azo bonds, which are specific arrangements of nitrogen atoms. Dyes formed in this way are called azo dyes.

Some azo dyes, called acid dyes, dissolve easily in water. Acid dyes react with animal fibers to form very stable coloring materials. However, acid dyes are unsuitable for use on plant fibers. In this case, another type of azo dye called a substantive, or direct dye, is used. Adding a salt during the dyeing process causes coloring agents to be formed inside the plant fibers.

Improved azo dyes

Modern azo dyes are colorfast, which means that they keep their colors well when they are exposed to sunlight. Their normal resistance to washing is not as good, however, especially at high temperatures. This property can be improved by treating the dyed material with various chemicals. Some acid dyes are mixed with metal salts to form metal-complex dyes. Direct dyes can be treated with chemicals to convert them to azoic dyes. Both metal-complex dyes and azoic dyes produce colors that do not fade in the wash or in sunlight.

Vat dyes

Vat dyes are mostly synthetic but include indigo, which can be natural or synthetic. Modern vat dyes are derived from anthracene and similar chemicals, and they are treated to make them dissolve in water. After dyeing, vat dyes are made insoluble again so they cannot be washed out of the material. Vat-dyed plant fibers are extremely colorfast to light and washing at high temperatures.

Sulfur dyes

Sulfur dyes become soluble in the presence of sodium sulfide. After dyeing, this chemical is made inactive and the dye becomes insoluble again.

Reactive dyes

Reactive dyes are formed from soluble azo or anthracene dyes by adding a highly reactive ingredient. This ingredient combines chemically with the cellulose of plant fibers. Reactive dyes are bright and will not fade. They are also easy to apply and are replacing vat dyes for many uses.

Disperse dyes

The dyes already mentioned are intended mainly for use with natural fibers. Some of these dyes work well with artificial fibers, but special new dyes had to be developed to treat acetate fiber. These coloring agents are called disperse dyes. They dissolve in acetate and color its surface at a temperature of about 180°F (82°C). Disperse dyes are also used for coloring polyester fibers.

Dyeing methods

When a material is dyed, either the material or the dye is kept moving. This is done to ensure a regular flow of dye through the material, so that the color produced does not vary. The material being dyed

▼ *Industrial dyeing is highly automated. First the fabric is soaked in a large vat of liquid dye, called a dye bath. It is then passed through a mangle, which squeezes out the excess liquid. A heater spreads and fixes the dye, and the fabric is washed to remove any excess dye. Finally, the fabric is dried in a large heater.*

◀ *A factory worker adds a green dye to a vat of candy. Most food dyes are taken from vegetable sources, and they are generally considered to be safe to eat. However, recent tests have shown that some artificial food dyes that were once thought to be safe to eat are in fact highly toxic. Most countries have removed these food dyes from their lists of approved additives.*

may be in the form of loose fiber, yarn, woven, or knitted fabric. The form in which the material is dyed depends on the type of product. Multicolored fabrics, for example, are made from yarns that were previously dyed different colors.

Loose fibers are pressed into perforated containers. The dye liquid is then pumped through. Yarns are wound onto perforated tubes through which the liquid is pumped. Woven fabrics can be dyed in a similar way on perforated beams. The fabric is kept moving—any unevenness in dyeing is immediately obvious on fabric. With yarn, a slightly lighter or darker section is hard to see once it has been made into fabric.

Dyeing is most effective at a high temperature, so all dyeing machines are heated. With polyester fibers, the required temperature is well above the normal boiling point of water. Thus the dyeing process has to be carried out in a sealed, high-pressure container. The high pressure prevents the liquid from boiling.

Dyeing food

Fabric is not the only material that is dyed. Many dyes are added to fresh and processed foods to make them look more appealing to eat. Many of the same food dyes are used as coloring additives in cosmetics and drugs. Since people eat food dyes, the Food and Drug Administration (FDA) strictly regulates the use of these additives.

See also: CHEMICAL REACTION • FIBER • FOOD TECHNOLOGY • PAINT • TEXTILE

Ear and hearing

The ear is a very delicate and complex organ that provides the senses of hearing and balance. What is usually called the ear is actually the outer ear, where sounds enter. The middle ear amplifies the sounds. The inner ear sends the messages to the brain.

The ear is an organ that receives and responds to sound. Sound is caused by tiny disturbances in the air. *Sound wave* is the name given to the movement of air that travels from the source of the sound to the ears. If someone is swimming underwater, he or she can still hear sounds because sound waves can travel through the water.

Sound cannot travel in outer space because there is nothing to carry the sound waves. An astronaut on a space walk needs a radio intercom to talk to fellow crew members.

The ear detects even faint noises and also analyzes them. It is extremely sensitive to tiny differences in the intensity of sound and the time of its arrival in each ear. This ability enables people to identify the source of a sound and also to listen to certain sounds while ignoring others.

Structure of the ear

The human ear is divided into three main parts—the outer ear, the middle ear, and the inner ear. The outer ear consists of the obvious fleshy flap on each side of the head, called the auricle or pinna, and a bony passage, called the ear canal, which leads to the eardrum. A waxy substance is secreted by the walls of the ear canal that prevents the skin from drying up and flaking. Too much wax, however, can cause problems—earache, deafness, and tinnitus (ringing in the ears).

Beyond the eardrum, inside the head, is the middle ear. This is a continuation of the ear canal. It contains three small bones, commonly called the

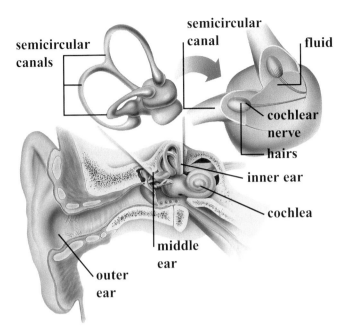

▲ *The ears provide people with the senses of hearing and balance. The outer ear receives sound vibrations from the outside world. These vibrations are amplified by the middle ear and then transmitted by the inner ear to the brain through the cochlear nerve. Balance is achieved through ear structures called semicircular canals. When the body moves, fluid in the canals causes minute hairs to bend. The nerves to which they are attached alert the brain to rebalance the body.*

stapes (meaning "stirrup" in Latin), the malleus (meaning "hammer" in Latin), and the incus (meaning "anvil" in Latin). The stapes is attached to the inner ear, the malleus is attached to the eardrum, and the incus connects the stapes and the malleus.

From the middle ear a narrow tube, called the eustachian tube, connects the ear with the throat. The eustachian tube equalizes air pressure on either side of the eardrum. When people fly in an airplane, the popping in their ears is caused by small movements of the eardrum brought about through changes of air pressure.

Deep inside the head is the inner ear, which is filled with a fluid called endolymph. The inner ear contains the semicircular canals, which control balance, and the spiral-shaped cochlea, which deals with hearing. The compartments of the inner ear are so complex that the inner ear as a whole is often called the labyrinth. The way in which sound is transmitted through the inner ear is very complex and not fully understood.

How we hear

When sound waves reach the ear, they are collected by the pinna, which acts like a funnel. The sound waves then travel down the ear canal and hit the eardrum, which is stretched tightly like a drum skin. The sound waves make the eardrum vibrate.

The eardrum passes these vibrations to the small connecting bones in the middle ear. Movement of the eardrum is amplified (strengthened) twenty times by this arrangement, and the vibrations are passed to the cochlea.

Like the rest of the inner ear, the cochlea is filled with a watery fluid called endolymph. It also contains a thin membrane that covers the coils of the cochlea. The membrane, called the basilar membrane, connects thousands of tiny nerve fibers to the cochlear nerve. When the endolymph and the basilar membrane vibrate, tiny hairs on the basilar membrane stimulate the nerve fibers, which

◀ *Music in nightclubs might be loud enough to cause permanent hearing damage. Recent estimates suggest that one in five young people have already put their hearing at risk because of exposure to loud music.*

▲ *A worker wears ear guards to protect his ears from the sound of a pneumatic drill. These hand tools can make a sound of more than 100 decibels. At this level, sounds can permanently damage one's hearing.*

DID YOU KNOW?

The loudness of sounds is measured on a scale of units called decibels. The bottom of this scale, 0 decibels, is fixed as the faintest sound that can be heard by the human ear. There is no top to the scale, but we cannot listen to sounds of more than 100 decibels without experiencing pain. Much louder sounds, such as explosions, can burst the eardrum.

send messages to the brain in the form of electrical impulses. The cochlear nerve runs to a part of the brain called the auditory, or hearing, center.

People hear a difference between high-pitched sounds and low-pitched sounds because these affect different parts of the basilar membrane. High-pitched sounds cause vibrations at the base of the cochlea. Lower-pitched, or deeper, sounds cause vibrations farther along the cochlea.

The ears and balance

To remain upright and steady requires accurate muscular control. The nervous system works with a part of the brain called the cerebellum to achieve balance. Messages bringing information about body position come from three sources—the joints, the eyes, and the semicircular canals. These messages are processed in the cerebellum.

Inflammation of the inner ear often results in disturbance of both hearing and balance. When their balance mechanism is disturbed, people feel dizzy and they might even fall over.

In most cases, dizziness is the result of spinning around too quickly. This sets off the movement of the endolymph, which continues to move even after the person has stopped spinning. An ice skater can prevent this from happening by turning his or her head in one swift movement, rather than turning it with the body.

See also: BRAIN • SOUND

Earth

Earth is the third planet from the Sun in the solar system. It is the fifth largest in size and has one natural satellite, called the Moon. Seen from space, Earth is covered by clouds and a vast expanse of blue ocean. The ice caps at the poles are a brilliant white and grasslands a light green brown.

Most people think that Earth is a perfect sphere, but in fact it is slightly flattened at the poles. If Earth were scaled down to the size of a basketball it would be impossible to see the flattening. All around this basketball-sized Earth, the atmosphere would be a thin film only ⅛ inch (0.3 centimeters) thick. The part of the atmosphere that people breathe would be no thicker than a coat of paint ¹⁄₂₀₀ inch (0.001 centimeters) thick. Mount Everest would stick up about the same distance, while the deepest ocean troughs would be scratches about ¹⁄₁₂₀ inch (0.002 centimeters) deep.

How old is Earth?

People once thought that Earth formed quite recently. In the 1600s, Irish scholar Bishop James Ussher (1581–1656) added up all the generations of people in the Bible, starting from Adam and Eve. Ussher concluded that Earth was created in 4004 BCE. As time went by, however, more accurate ways were found of measuring how old Earth's rocks are. The oldest rocks found so far date back more than 3.7 billion years. The solar system is even older than that. Meteors have been dated back to 4.5 billion years ago. Most scientists now think that Earth is about 4.6 billion years old.

When Earth first formed, it was a blazing ball covered by molten rock. Volcanoes spurted out liquid rock to form a thin crust. Very slowly the crust cooled and cracked. Poisonous gases seeped out of the rocks, forming an atmosphere. Water vapor also came from the rocks. Clouds formed for the first time and torrential rain poured from the skies. The downpour lasted for millions of years, and water collected to form the oceans.

It was in these early oceans that the first living things came into being—primitive plants. As the plants evolved over millions of years, they produced more and more oxygen. Earth's atmosphere became more like it is today.

Inside Earth

In the seething inferno that was the new Earth, heavy substances sank down into the center. Most heavy substances were metals—largely iron and some nickel. Lighter substances, specifically silicate minerals (rocks containing the elements silicon and oxygen), stayed at Earth's surface. The outermost layer of Earth cooled over millions of years to form a solid crust.

◀ *This is an image of Earth as seen from outer space. More than 70 percent of Earth's surface is covered by water.*

473

▲ *Water vapor formed as Earth evolved, creating rain that filled the oceans. This water, combined with Earth's distance from the Sun, created a unique climate that was ideal for sustaining life.*

The crust is thickest under the continents, where it is about 20 miles (35 kilometers) thick. Under the oceans, it is much thinner—only about 3½ miles (6 kilometers) thick. It is not one perfect layer; rather it is split up into a number of plates.

The crust lies on a rocky layer called the mantle. The mantle is about 1,800 miles (2,900 kilometers) thick, and it is divided into an outer region and an inner region. Since pressures and temperatures increase with depth inside Earth, the inner mantle is slightly melted.

The metallic outer core is completely molten. This part of the mantle is around 1,250 miles (2,000 kilometers) thick. The inner core is solid. It is about 1,700 miles (2,740 kilometers) in diameter.

Geologists have figured out Earth's internal structure by studying the way in which seismic waves travel through the planet. The waves change speed as they travel through the different layers.

Continental plates

The mantle allows Earth's continental plates to move around. These plates are always moving, but very slowly. Rocks are always being added to the plates in some places, pushing the plates apart.

DID YOU KNOW?

Earth is a planet of many extremes, which is illustrated by the following examples.
• The coldest temperature recorded on Earth was −126.9°F (−88.3°C) at Vostok, Antarctica, in 1960.
• The hottest temperature recorded was 136.4°F (57.7°C) at Al 'Aziziyah, Libya, in 1922.
• The driest place on Earth is Arica in Chile. It averages ³⁄₁₀₀ inch (0.076 centimeters) of rain each year.
• The highest annual average rainfall is at Mount Waialeale, Hawaii, which records 460 inches (1,168 centimeters).

When two plates meet, one may be forced underneath the other. This movement is seldom smooth. It happens in sudden jerks, and these great jerks can trigger earthquakes.

Continental drift has been going on throughout Earth's history. It is believed that around 170 million years ago there was originally just one huge land mass, called Pangaea. Over millions of years, Pangaea slowly split to create the continents. The continental plates drifted farther and farther apart, resulting in Earth's continents today.

How Earth moves

Earth moves in quite a complex way, but it has three main movements. One movement is the rotation of Earth around its axis. This is a line though the center of the planet between the North and South Poles. This rotation takes 24 hours and is the reason Earth has a night and a day. Earth also orbits (revolves around) the Sun with the other planets. One complete orbit around the Sun takes Earth one year, or, more accurately, 365 days, 6 hours, 9 minutes, and 10 seconds. Earth travels around the Sun at a speed of about 18½ miles (29.8 kilometers)

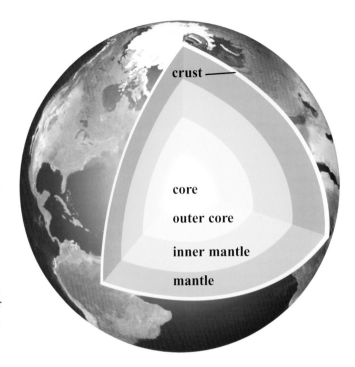

▲ *Earth consists of several distinct layers. These layers surround a hot metal core, which has a temperature of about 10,300°F (5700°C). The solid outer crust is fairly thin and moves slowly on top of the underlying mantle.*

▼ *This North American desert landscape is an example of the way in which Earth's surface varies widely, depending on factors such as climate and erosion.*

Northern summer and southern winter occur when the Northern Hemisphere is tilted toward the Sun.

Northern winter and southern summer occur when the Northern Hemisphere is tilted away from the Sun.

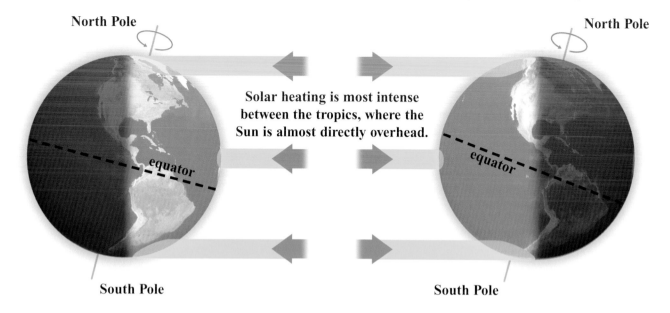

North Pole

equator

South Pole

Solar heating is most intense between the tropics, where the Sun is almost directly overhead.

North Pole

equator

South Pole

per second. Finally, Earth travels around our galaxy, called the Milky Way, with the Sun and everything else in the solar system.

Earth rotates about its axis from west to east. This rotation makes it appear that the Sun, Moon, and stars move across the sky from east to west. Earth's axis of rotation is tilted so that the North Pole always points to part of the sky near the Pole Star. It is this constant tilting that causes the seasons. As Earth moves around the Sun, first one pole and then the other is tilted toward the Sun. This means that places in the Northern Hemisphere have summer while those in the Southern Hemisphere have winter and vice versa.

Solar heating

Life on Earth depends on heat from the Sun. Temperatures vary, however, largely because the amount of the Sun's energy that reaches Earth varies from place to place. Earth is roughly round like a sphere, so the Sun's rays are spread over a much larger area near the North and South Poles than they are at the equator. (The equator is an imaginary line around Earth exactly halfway between the poles. It divides Earth into two hemispheres, or half-spheres.) At the equator, the Sun's rays strike Earth's atmosphere more or less

▲ *Earth tilts at an angle of 23½ degrees from the vertical in relation to the Sun. As a result, the day length, and hence the amount of solar energy reaching different parts of the world, varies. As Earth orbits the Sun, Earth's tilt causes the seasons.*

head on. Toward the poles, the Sun's rays strike the atmosphere at a slanting angle. Near the poles, therefore, the Sun's rays pass through a greater thickness of atmosphere before reaching Earth, and the atmosphere absorbs more energy than at the equator. The higher concentration of the Sun's rays at the equator is the reason why equatorial regions are the hottest on Earth.

The lengths of day and night are also important in determining how much solar energy reaches Earth. On September 23 and March 21, the length of day and night are equal all over the world, at 12 hours each. These days are called the equinoxes, which means "equal night." After March 21 in the Northern Hemisphere, and after September 23 in the Southern Hemisphere, days get longer and the nights shorter. Longer days mean more sunlight for

▼ *Trees take on a characteristic color during the fall— the transitional season between summer and winter. In midlatitudes, between the tropics and the Arctic and Antarctic Circles, there are four seasons. Nearer the equator and the poles, there are fewer distinct seasons.*

DID YOU KNOW?

Here are some of the most important facts and figures about Earth.

- Diameter, equatorial: 7,927 miles (12,757 kilometers)
- Diameter, polar: 7,900 miles (12,714 kilometers)
- Circumference, equatorial: 24,902 miles (40,075 kilometers)
- Circumference, polar: 24,860 miles (40,007 kilometers)
- Distance from Sun: 92,960,000 miles (149,600,000 kilometers)
- Spins on axis in 23 hours 56 minutes 4 seconds
- Speed in orbit: 18½ miles per second (29.8 kilometers per second)
- Orbits Sun in 365 days, 6 hours, 9 minutes, and 10 seconds

places well to the north and south of the equator. This helps balance the loss of energy caused by the absorption of heat by the atmosphere.

The solar year

In relation to the Sun, Earth's axis tilts at an angle of 23½ degrees from the vertical. For half the year, the Northern Hemisphere leans more toward the Sun and so gets more sunlight than the Southern Hemisphere. For the rest of the year, the Southern Hemisphere leans toward the Sun, while the Northern Hemisphere leans away from it.

One effect of Earth's tilt is that the North and South Poles have six months of continuous daylight, when the Sun never sets, and six months of continuous darkness. In addition, everywhere north of the Arctic Circle (latitude 66 degrees 33 minutes north) and south of the Antarctic Circle (66 degrees 33 minutes south) there is at least one day of continuous daylight. This figure rises for places closer to the poles. These regions in the Northern and Southern Hemispheres are called

▲ *The poles are the coldest places on Earth, because of the tilt of Earth. These regions receive the least solar energy and have long, dark, bitterly cold winters.*

"lands of the midnight Sun." Lines of latitude are measured from the equator (0 degrees) to the poles (90 degrees north and 90 degrees south).

The Northern Hemisphere is tilted toward the Sun at its greatest extent on June 21. Astronomers call this day the summer solstice in the Northern Hemisphere and the winter solstice in the Southern Hemisphere. On this day, the Sun is overhead at the Tropic of Cancer (an imaginary line of latitude at 23 degrees 27 minutes north). After June 21, Earth continues its journey and the Northern Hemisphere starts to tilt less far away from the Sun. On September 23, the Sun is overhead at the equator. This is the autumn equinox in the Northern Hemisphere and the spring equinox in the Southern Hemisphere.

On September 23, the Southern Hemisphere starts to lean toward the Sun, reaching its maximum tilt on about December 22. On this day, the Sun is overhead at the Tropic of Capricorn, an imaginary line of latitude at 23 degrees 27 minutes south. This is the summer solstice in the Southern Hemisphere and the winter solstice in the Northern Hemisphere. By March 21, the Sun has again moved overhead at the equator. This day is the spring equinox in the Northern Hemisphere and the autumn equinox in the Southern Hemisphere.

The seasons

The seasons are the periods of the year. Northern lands have a spring from March to May, a summer from June to August, a fall from September to November, and a winter from December to February. Seasons in southern countries are the opposite of these. Countries in the middle belt around Earth often have only wet and dry seasons, or their climate may be the same all year round.

Near the equator and the poles, seasons are not as different from one another as in the middle latitudes. In some places near the equator, it is hot and wet throughout the year. In other parts, there are rainy and dry seasons, both of them hot. In polar regions, the changes between winter and summer occur so quickly that there are really only two seasons: a long, bitterly cold winter and a brief, mild summer.

See also: ATMOSPHERE • CLIMATE • PLATE TECTONICS • SOLAR SYSTEM • WEATHER SYSTEM

Earthmover

Before any bridge, building, or freeway can be built, the ground on which the structure will be supported must be prepared. Vast amounts of loose earth have to be dug up and cleared away. This is the job of the earthmover.

Modern construction relies on the "muscle" of giant earthmovers to tackle jobs such as digging trenches or excavating the foundations for larger buildings. An earthmover, such as a power shovel, is a simple machine. It has a long, jointed arm with a bucket at the end. The edge of the bucket is lined with sharp teeth to scoop out soil.

The arm and the bucket are controlled by hydraulic (operated by pressurized fluid) jacks worked by the driver. When the bucket has been filled, the driver turns the top part of the power shovel, including the driver's cabin, around to a waiting removal truck and dumps the debris.

The basic method of earthmoving remains unchanged from the earliest times. It is just the machines that have been modernized. There are several kinds of earthmover today that can handle any kind of material from mud to broken rock.

Dragline excavators

The dragline excavator works with wire rope (rather than hydraulics) and is carried along on caterpillar tracks. It has a digging bucket hung from a long jib (arm) by a cable. The dragline (wire rope) is fixed to the bucket and wound around a winch at the base of the jib. To operate, the bucket is swung forward onto the ground, and it fills as it is dragged back along the ground by the dragline.

Dragline excavators are commonly used when the soil is partly submerged in water, and also when heavy materials need to be lifted. Such machines are

▼ A caterpillar-tracked excavator loads earth into a dump truck. The digging bucket and excavator arm are both operated by powerful hydraulic pistons.

479

A dragline excavator loads earth into a large dump truck. Dragline excavators have larger buckets than hydraulic excavators and are used particularly in quarries.

particularly useful in demolition work. Not only do they collect and clear the rubble, they also help in the demolition itself. A steel ball in place of the bucket can be used to demolish buildings. Some of these machines can weigh more than 3,000 tons (2,721 tonnes), and have buckets that can hold over 100 tons (90 tonnes) of earth.

Bucket-wheel excavators

Bucket-wheel excavators are designed to cut away earth from the sides of a bank or slope using a series of buckets mounted on the rim of a large wheel. As the wheel turns, the soil is tipped onto a conveyor belt and carried away to a truck or a tip. Bucket-wheel excavators are also useful in strip mines and quarries. There are economic advantages to this continuous operation, as more time is spent digging than carrying and maneuvering.

Bulldozers and angledozers

Bulldozers were first developed in the 1920s. They are similar to tractors but have a wide steel blade at the front, which is curved from top to bottom. This shape helps roll the load, so that it can be pushed more easily. The blade can be raised or lowered by means of a winch and cable or hydraulic power.

A typical bulldozer weighs from 6 to 40 tons (5.4 and 36 tonnes) and has a diesel engine, often producing several hundred horsepower. The machine is a modified crawler tractor. It moves on a pair of caterpillar tracks instead of wheels. The metal tracks enable the bulldozer to move easily over rough ground, where a wheeled vehicle would get stuck. However, a tracked vehicle cannot travel at high speed. The maximum speed of a bulldozer is 6 miles per hour (10 kilometers per hour). Bulldozers play an important part in clearing the land on new building sites.

An angledozer is a bulldozer with one side of its blade mounted farther forward than the other side. Since the blade is tilted in this way, the load is pushed to one side when the bulldozer moves forward. Snow plows are examples of angledozers.

Loaders

The loader was developed after the bulldozer. While a bulldozer has a wide blade at the front, the loader has a large, tooth-rimmed mechanical shovel for lifting the load.

Crawler loaders, mounted on caterpillar tracks, are often confused with bulldozers. Commonly used on demolition sites and rough construction sites, crawler loaders can maneuver and operate in small areas. They can work on broken rock, concrete, or other jagged surfaces because they lack tires, which would be ruined. With good ground surface, wheeled loaders, which turn and move with more speed, can be used.

Scrapers

Motor scrapers are used for removing the surface layer of a construction site, most often where a highway is being constructed or resurfaced. The scraper is really nothing more than a giant box open at the front and mounted on large wheels and driven by a diesel engine. As the vehicle moves forward, the box fills with the aid of a loading edge that can be pushed a little way into the ground.

In soil too soft to hold heavy loads, a scraper trailer is used. This trailer is a large scraper box mounted on wheels and pulled along behind a tractor-type machine on caterpillar treads.

Dumpers

Earthmovers are not built to travel with their loads over long distances. Most depend on support vehicles to do that part of the job. Often standard trucks can be used, but where the terrain is more broken up, then dump trucks with four-wheel drive are more dependable. These trucks are large and very sturdy machines that can carry from 20 tons

(18.1 tonnes) up to 200 tons (181 tonnes). For maximum results, the dumper's capacity and size are matched to that of the excavator or loader. The maximum capacity for two-wheel drive vehicles is 100 tons (90 tonnes), but 50-ton (45-tonne) vehicles are most common.

All dumpers come with a tipper to release the loose earth. This tipper is usually powered by a jack driven by the engine or by hydraulic arms. A number of small dumper trucks carry their loads in a large bin in front of the driver. To dump the load, the driver pulls a lever that tips the bin forward. Such small dumpers are powered by diesel engines and driven by their front wheels, while the steering acts on the rear wheels. These small dumpers are frequently used on building sites.

Dredgers

Dredgers are floating machines used to keep harbors, canals, and rivers free from mud and silt. They also collect gravel and sand for construction, and they mine diamonds, gold, tin, and other minerals from the inshore seabed.

The first power dredgers were of the bucket type, and many of these machines are still in use today. Bucket dredgers use a chain-and-bucket conveyor

▼ *A fleet of bulldozers gather sand from an area of desert. The sand is being collected for use in construction. Bulldozers are used where the material to be moved is loose and can be pushed along.*

▲ *A grab dredger removes silt from the entrance to a harbor. The hopper barge will dump the silt elsewhere.*

system, strung on a long frame. The frame can be raised or lowered hydraulically to the correct angle at the bottom.

Bucket dredgers must be towed to the dredging site by a tugboat. They are used in conjunction with hopper barges. These craft transport the dredged-up material out to sea, where it is dumped through a midship section in the barge. The dredger itself is secured with anchors and can be moved by pulling in one anchor cable and letting out another.

Other similar dredgers are dipper dredgers and scoop dredgers. Dipper dredgers have a big shovel scoop that pivots on the end of a long arm, or boom. Grab dredgers have a scoop like a clamshell, with a pair of large, hinged jaws. This scoop is suspended by cables from the end of a boom.

Grab dredgers and dipper dredgers can be moved about more easily than bucket dredgers. They can also work in awkward corners and close to harbor walls. Some of them are self-propelled and have their own hoppers so that they can transport their own spoil (mud and silt) to the dumping ground.

Dipper and grab dredgers are usually secured by lines and anchors when they are working. Deck winches haul the dredger into position. The dredgers are also often fitted with legs which can be extended to the bottom.

Another type of dredger is the suction dredger. There are different designs of suction dredger, but they all use powerful pumps. The pumps suck up water and solid material from the bottom through a large tube. Some dredgers have several pumps operating at the same time.

When the material to be dredged is sand or gravel, the tubes can be used by themselves. Suction drag-arm dredgers, for example, have an ordinary seagoing hull like a boat, with a suction arm fixed underneath. This arm is dragged across the bottom as the vessel moves along. Hoppers for the spoil are built into the hull of the vessel. Drag-arm dredgers are the most efficient type of dredger.

For other uses, the suction tubes are used with machines that cut and scrape the bottom material to break it up. Cutterhead dredgers, for example, have a revolving cutter at the end of a boom. The sucking end of the suction tube is placed near the cutter to suck up the spoil as it is broken up.

Some suction dredgers have extendible legs that can be used in shallow water. Some have long floating pipelines that can be extended some distance from the ship to dump the spoil as soon as it is sucked up. Suction dredgers can also be fitted with chutes that deliver the spoil to waiting barges or dockside dump trucks.

Suction dredgers are often used in projects to reclaim land. In this case, they suck up spoil from the sea bottom and pump the solids straight over a nearby embankment into the area to be filled up. Water picked up with the solids during the suction operation is allowed to spill out by means of drains in the pumping tube.

The largest modern dredgers have hoppers that can hold up to 30,000 tons (27,210 tonnes) of solid spoil. Big dredging operations have been made necessary by the large size and great depth of water needed by modern freight ships and supertankers. These great ships require large-scale excavations near their docksides.

See also: BUILDING TECHNIQUES • CRANE • WINCH AND WINDLASS

Earthquake

Earthquakes are sudden and violent shifts within Earth that shake the land and can cause much destruction in just a few minutes. Scientists are trying to solve the problem of how to predict an earthquake and so evacuate people before towns collapse.

There are some parts of the world where earthquakes are a constant threat—sometimes causing only minor tremors, and other times catastrophic results. These earthquake-prone areas have one thing in common. They all lie along relatively narrow and unstable sections of Earth's crust. These unstable sections are the boundaries of plates in Earth's crust. These plates are constantly jamming and jarring against each other, forcing tremendous pressure up through Earth's crust to be released as earthquakes or volcanic eruptions.

Moving plates

The plates that make up Earth's crust move slowly. This movement is partly maintained by new rock constantly forming along the edges of adjoining oceanic plates. As new rock forms, the ocean plates are pushed apart. Molten rock from beneath Earth's crust can force its way out along these boundaries, called divergent plate boundaries, because the crust is much thinner under the oceans. The divergent plate boundaries are marked by great ocean ridges.

▼ *Many people who are killed in earthquakes die because they live in buildings that are poorly built, such as this apartment building in Turkey.*

▲ *Rescuers bring a man out from the rubble alive, after an earthquake in Bingol, Turkey, in May 2003. The earthquake demolished dozens of homes and killed at least 84 people.*

The deepest parts of the ocean, the ocean trenches, also mark the edges of plates. Where an ocean plate meets the edge of a continental plate, the ocean plate is forced beneath the thicker continental plate. This is called a subductive plate boundary.

Both these types of plate movement explain why the continents have drifted apart and continue to drift. Earthquakes occur along both divergent and subductive plate boundaries. Because of their locations on the edges of oceanic and continental plates, they are often not very destructive.

Fault lines

The most destructive types of earthquake are associated with cracks in the crustal plates. These cracks are called faults. Pressures from within Earth place great strain along these faults, and every so often the two sides slip, causing an earthquake. The two sides of the fault are forced up, down, or alongside each other. Normal faulting occurs when one side of the fault is forced up against the other. Reverse faulting occurs when one side is forced underneath the other. In transverse or strike-slip faulting, the two sides of the fault move alongside each other.

The San Andreas fault is a transform fault that runs along the west coast of the United States. It is 596 miles (960 kilometers) long and caused, among others, the devastating San Francisco earthquake of 1906. A violent movement of the fault edges near the city caused many buildings to collapse, and broken gas pipes caused fires to sweep the city.

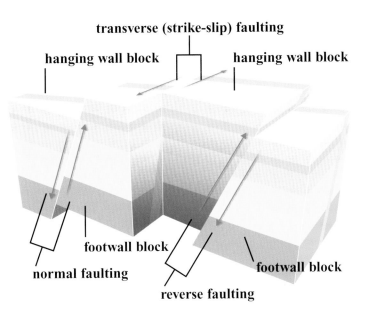

transverse (strike-slip) faulting

hanging wall block

hanging wall block

footwall block

normal faulting

footwall block

reverse faulting

▲ *In normal faulting, the hanging wall block moves down relative to the footwall block. In reverse faulting, the hanging wall block moves up. In transverse faulting, the sides of the fault are forced alongside each other.*

▼ *The most devastating earthquake to hit the United States was the California earthquake of May 19, 1906. The city of San Francisco was largely destroyed.*

Predicting earthquakes

Earthquakes can take a heavy toll in human life. One earthquake in China in 1556 killed an estimated 800,000 people. More recently in 2004, a massive earthquake off the coast of Indonesia caused a tsunami that killed more than 225,000 people in India, Southeast Asia, and the east coast of Africa. Millions were made homeless in the aftermath of the disaster. Finding ways to tell when earthquakes are going to occur can help save lives.

One way is to study the behavior of animals immediately before disaster strikes. The Chinese adopted this method in 1975, evacuating the population of Haicheng in Manuchuria on the same day that a massive earthquake flattened 90 percent of the town. The evacuation was made on the basis of strange animal behavior in the area.

Research has been conducted around the world to test whether animals—or indeed humans—have some way of sensing an earthquake. Tests are still inconclusive, but it has been established that some animals do strange things before an earthquake.

▲ *This elevated highway has collapsed after an earthquake in California in 1994. Elevated highways and bridges are particularly vulnerable to earthquakes.*

Many, more scientific, approaches to earthquake predicting are also taken. One is a 3-mile-deep (5-kilometer) hole drilled in southern California. Geologists use the hole as a point from which to study the nearby San Andreas fault. They are hoping to find out what causes friction in the deep cracks in Earth's crust as a way of learning the geological signs that precede an earthquake.

Shockwaves

A single earthquake can cause three main types of shockwaves—P (Primary), S (Secondary), and L (Long) waves. P waves alternately compress and expand and vibrate in the direction of travel. They pass through solids, liquids, and gases. S waves pass through solids only and are slower than P waves. They vibrate at right angles to the direction of the wave and are the "shake" waves. The last shock waves to be picked up are the L waves, which pass through only the surface of Earth's crust. L waves have a long wavelength and are the most destructive of the shockwaves. They travel more slowly than P and S waves but can travel long distances—sometimes several times around Earth.

Measuring earthquakes

The science of measuring earthquakes is called seismology. U.S. scientist C. F. Richter (1900–1985) devised a formula in 1935 for calculating the strength of an earthquake from instrument readings of its magnitude. The formula is based upon the amount of energy released by the rock movements at the point of origin (the focus) rather than upon surface damage. Richter then created a scale to compare earthquake strengths. The Richter scale goes from 1 to 9. Each higher number means a ten-fold increase in the earthquake's strength.

Seismographs are instruments used to measure the force of an earthquake. They can detect the focus source as well as the type of shock wave produced. Shallow earthquakes have a focus above the boundary that is between Earth's crust and the deeper mantle layer—22 miles (35 kilometers) deep. Intermediate earthquakes have a focus between this and 190 miles (300 kilometers), while deep earthquakes lie usually between 310 and 435 miles (500 to 700 kilometers) from the surface.

The strength, or magnitude, of an earthquake is measured on the Richter scale. Earthquakes measuring 2 are barely noticeable, but an 8 on the scale means an extremely violent tremor. The most powerful earthquake yet measured was 8.9.

There is a worldwide network of seismological stations with interconnecting communications systems. Scientists can quickly calculate the focus, strength, and epicenter (the point on Earth's surface directly above the area of disturbance) of an earthquake and pass on the vital data.

In the United States, there are 525 seismographs buried 200 feet (61 meters) underground in Montana. These seismographs are able to detect seismic waves that might occur in almost any corner of the world. It takes this sensitive equipment just 10 seconds to register a tremor, and it will record earth movements as tiny as a millionth of a meter.

See also: BUILDING TECHNIQUES •
PLATE TECTONICS • SEISMOLOGY • VOLCANO

Eclipse

Eclipses occur when one object passes in front of something that shines and then blocks the light from the shining object. Objects such as the Sun and the Moon in space result in some of the most spectacular examples of eclipses. These events provide astronomers with important information about celestial bodies and faraway galaxies.

One example of an eclipse happens when a person holds her hand between her eyes and a burning candle. The person's hand blocks the light of the flame from reaching the eye, and the candle is said to be in eclipse. However, most people now use the word *eclipse* to refer to the various events that occur in space.

Solar eclipses

The most spectacular eclipses are solar eclipses. Solar eclipses occur when the Moon passes between Earth and the Sun, and Earth lies in the Moon's shadow.

Solar eclipses are either total or partial. During a total solar eclipse, the Sun, the Moon, and Earth form a perfectly straight line in space. The Moon covers the Sun's disk completely, and the faint ring of sunlight, called the corona, shines out around the black disk. Day turns into night as the Moon's shadow races across Earth. This shadow sweeps out a path of total eclipse up to 150 miles (250 kilometers) across. People must be within this shadow to see a total eclipse. When the Moon does not cover the Sun's disk completely during a total eclipse, an "annular" eclipse occurs, and the dark Moon is surrounded by a bright ring. Annular eclipses occur because the orbits of the Moon and Earth around the Sun are not perfect circles. During a partial solar eclipse, the alignment of the Sun, the Moon, and Earth is not perfectly straight, so the Moon covers only part of the Sun's disk.

▲ *The diamond-ring effect occurs at the beginning and end of totality during a total solar eclipse. As the faint corona around the Sun is just becoming visible, the final rays of sunlight shine around the Moon's surface like a ring with a glittering diamond on it.*

Lunar eclipses

A lunar eclipse occurs when Earth comes between the Moon and the Sun. As the Moon shines only by reflected sunlight, when Earth blocks the Sun from shining on it, the Moon can no longer be seen from Earth. Earth casts a shadow that covers the Moon either partially or completely. During this time, the Moon takes on a pale copper red color. Lunar eclipses occur only during a full moon.

> **DID YOU KNOW?**
>
> By a remarkable coincidence, the Moon and the Sun look about the same size from Earth. The Sun is about 400 times larger than the Moon in diameter, but it is also 400 times farther away than the Moon. For this reason, the Moon can cover the Sun's disk completely.

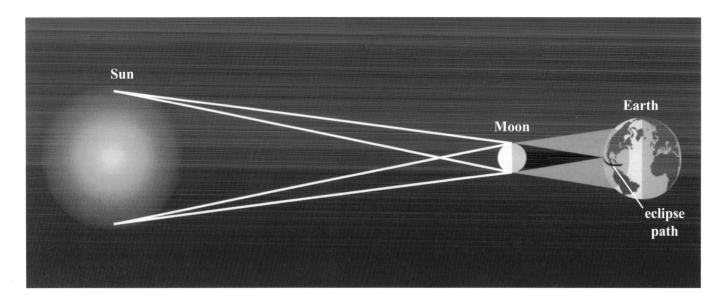

Sun

Moon

Earth

eclipse
path

▲ *During a solar eclipse, the shadow of the Moon follows a narrow path across Earth's surface. The area in which an observer can see the total eclipse is called the zone of totality.*

How often do eclipses occur?

Eclipses do not happen very often, and most are not total—the entire Sun or Moon does not disappear. On average, there are between two and five partial solar eclipses and one or two lunar eclipses each year. Total solar eclipses occur somewhere on Earth once every one or two years.

The reason there are so few eclipses is that the Moon does not orbit Earth in the same plane as Earth orbits the Sun. Imagine a straight line drawn from the Sun to Earth and extended out from Earth on the other side. If the Moon always passed through this line as it orbits Earth, there would be two eclipses each month—a solar eclipse when the Moon came between Earth and the Sun and a lunar eclipse when Earth came between the Moon and the Sun. However, the Moon's orbit around Earth is tilted away from Earth's orbit around the Sun. As a result, there is far less chance that all three bodies will align along the same plane.

Observing an eclipse

Solar eclipses yield valuable information about the structure of the Sun. In normal circumstances, it is difficult to study features such as the corona since they are lost in the glare of sunlight. Since total eclipses of the Sun are rare, astronomers from all over the world travel vast distances to study them. Astronomers can figure out far in advance when the eclipse will happen and where the zone of totality will be. However, eclipse or not, no one should ever look at the Sun, either through a telescope or with the naked eye. Astronomers avoid damaging their eyes by using solar telescopes to project the Sun's image onto screens.

Solar effects

As Earth is plunged into darkness during a total solar eclipse, stars appear in the sky, animals behave as if it were nighttime, and the air grows chilly. Just before and just after the eclipse is total, something called the diamond-ring effect happens, and for a few seconds it appears as though a diamond is flashing at one side of the ring. Another effect, called "Bailey's Beads," occurs about the same time. Bailey's Beads are white patches that appear around the edge of the Moon just before and after a total eclipse. The white patches are caused by sunlight outlining mountains on the surface of the Moon. In addition, there are red prominences—huge eruptions of hot gas many times the size of Earth—that shoot out from the Sun's surface. These can be seen shining around the Moon.

See also: ASTRONOMY • EARTH • MOON • SUN

Ecology

Ecology is the branch of science concerned with the relationships of living things and their physical environment. German zoologist Ernst Haeckel coined the term *ecology* in 1869. It comes from the Greek word *oikos,* meaning "place to live."

All living things affect other living things. People are part of the living world and so they, too, are part of the study of ecology. Many different organisms affect people, from the tiniest bacteria to the largest tree. However, people can change their environment in a way that no other living thing can. For example, people clear forests to grow crops and to build houses to live in. These activities may be very destructive to plants and other animals.

Ecosystems

All the living and nonliving parts of an environment make up an ecosystem. The animals and plants in an ecosystem form what ecologists call a community. Ecosystems may be small, such as a pond, or enormous, such as a tropical savanna in Africa. If one part of an ecosystem suddenly changes, then the whole ecosystem is affected in some way. A failure to understand how delicately balanced ecosystems work can cause serious problems.

For example, many fish species have become severely depleted because of overfishing. Signs of overfishing are often obvious, for example, the lack

▼ *Farmers burn part of the Amazon rain forest to grow crops. Slash-and-burn agriculture has been practiced for hundreds of years by farmers around the world. As more people farm the land to feed the ever-growing human population, slash and burn has started to deplete the Amazon's unique biodiversity.*

▶ *Chilean fishers net several hundred tons of jack mackerel in a net called a purse seine. The single greatest threat to marine ecology is overfishing. Purse seines are also known to injure and kill marine mammals, especially dolphins.*

of catch for fishers. Another sign includes the sudden boom of other marine species that the fish once preyed on. Ecosystems can be affected by the declining fish population. Coral reefs and seaweed beds can be eaten alive by marine animals, such as sea urchins, without fish to control these grazers.

Biomes

Extremely large ecosystems with broadly similar ecological conditions are called biomes. These regions are chiefly distinguished by climate, which is the main factor in determining vegetation. The major land biomes are polar desert; tundra; taiga (coniferous forest); temperate forest; tropical forest, including rain forest; temperate grassland; tropical grassland; shrubland; and desert and semidesert. Other biomes include regions of freshwater (rivers, lakes, and wetlands), and the oceans, which include several distinct biomes, such as sunlit layers and ocean trenches.

Mountains and highland zones are a special case, because the climate changes with altitude (height above sea level). As a result, the highest mountains contain bands of vegetation that vary according to the temperature. Near the equator, mountains contain several bands of vegetation (biomes), ranging from tropical forest at the bottom to polar desert at the top.

Adaptations

Within each biome, a tremendous variety of living things has evolved, each of which has adapted to its environment over generations. For example, animals in the polar desert must keep warm and so

DID YOU KNOW?

For the past few decades, the United States and Canada have experienced rainfall that is ten times more acidic than normal. Habitats have been harmed as sulfur dioxide (SO_2) and nitrogen oxides (NOx) pollute the atmosphere, react with water and other chemicals in the atmosphere, and fall to Earth as acid rain. Acid rain damages everything from trees and soils, to fish and people. In the United States, burning fossil fuels, such as coal for electric power generation, is the main cause of acid rain.

they often have thick fur or more body fat than animals in warmer biomes. Animals in the world's grasslands must be able to move quickly to escape predators, because there is little cover in which to hide. Desert plants and animals must be able to survive on small amounts of water. Since they cannot move, plants, even more than animals, must be perfectly suited to their environment. By contrast, birds can migrate over long distances according to the season.

Changing ecosystems

Ecosystems often change naturally, for example, when a pond dries up. Larger organisms then have to compete for a smaller space and more limited resources. Eventually, larger organisms generally move away to find another habitat or they die.

Ecosystems may undergo a series of changes over a period of time. When a volcanic island emerges above the waves, for example, it is covered by lifeless ash and hardened lava. Tiny organisms, such as algae, quickly populate the island. Gradually, the weather breaks down the surface of the rocks to form soil, in which seeds brought by the wind sprout into plants. These so-called pioneer plants then provide food for animals on the island.

Ecologists call these gradual developments colonization. Over hundreds of years, the plant community undergoes a series of changes, which ecologists call a succession. The final stage of a succession is the climax community, which is made up of hundreds of plant species.

For example, the climax community of much of western and central Europe and the eastern United States was once deciduous forest, containing trees such as oaks. However, this climax community has been destroyed to make way for agriculture.

Niches

Animal life on Earth is extremely diverse. Some animals eat nuts and seeds, while others eat grasses or leaves. Other animals are carnivores (meat eaters), which eat other carnivores or herbivores (plant eaters). Ecologists call the job an animal does in nature, and its way of life, its niche. If two species come to occupy the same niche—that is, they are competing for the same food—one species will either move away, die out, or evolve.

▼ *Grand Teton National Park in Wyoming covers nearly 310,300 acres (125,550 hectares) and protects a wide range of wildlife and plant species.*

◀ *These children have decided to plant saplings as part of a school conservation program. The saplings will grow into new trees and regenerate the forest.*

Human interference in these cycles often has a bad effect on the environment. An example is the use of an insecticide called dichlorodiphenyltrichloroethane (DDT) in agriculture. Through the water cycle, DDT has spread from agricultural land to the depths of the oceans and the farthermost polar deserts. Although the use of DDT is now restricted by most countries, it has already made its way into the food people eat.

Similarly, nitrogen compounds, called nitrates, are used as fertilizers. If too much is used, however, the nitrates are washed into rivers and lakes, where they make plants and algae grow too quickly. These living things use up the oxygen in the water, and so fishes and other water animals die.

Ecology and conservation
Natural habitats and their living communities are being destroyed to make way for cities and farms. In many places, where forests have been cut down and grasslands plowed up, intensive agriculture and overgrazing have caused soil erosion, making formerly fertile areas barren. In many parts of the world, the air, land, and water have all been polluted by domestic and industrial waste, oil spillages, pesticides and insecticides, and automobile exhaust gases.

The science of maintaining Earth's biodiversity is called conservation. Many people try to protect animals and plants and the environment in which they live. Conservation also covers the protection of Earth's natural resources. Simple measures, such as recycling garbage and limiting the use of water, are forms of conservation. Other methods used by conservationists include activities such as habitat protection and breeding endangered animals in zoos. Without conservation, many animals and plants would soon become extinct.

Natural cycles
Nothing is ever lost in nature. It is simply recycled. The study of natural cycles is another important aspect of ecology. For example, water flows into the oceans through rivers. However, the Sun evaporates water from the oceans, forming clouds of water vapor. Rain clouds bring a supply of fresh water to land, seas, and rivers. This continuous process is called the water cycle.

In the carbon cycle, plants use the gas carbon dioxide (CO_2) in the air to make sugars, which are consumed by animals as carbohydrates. When the animals die, their bodies decompose. The carbon compounds locked up inside their bodies break down into smaller carbon compounds, which are taken up by plants again. Similar cycles exist for the elements nitrogen and phosphorus.

See also: BIOMES AND HABITATS • CLIMATE • EARTH • FOOD WEB • PHOTOSYNTHESIS

Edison, Thomas

Thomas Edison is considered by many to be one of the greatest inventors in history. By the time he died in 1931, he had patented more than one thousand inventions, including the first widely used electric lightbulb and the phonograph.

Thomas Alva Edison was born in Milan, Ohio, on February 11, 1847. In 1854, his father, Samuel, became the lighthouse keeper and carpenter on the Fort Gratiot military post near Port Huron, Michigan. Alva, as he was known until much later, started school there. Edison was an imaginative and inquisitive student, but he was bored. After three months he was expelled by his teacher, who claimed Edison's brain was "addled." After that, Edison's schooling was very sporadic. His mother undertook most of his education, and Edison also taught himself by reading avidly.

When he was ten, Edison set up a laboratory in the basement of his home. There, he experimented with chemistry and electricity and built a telegraph set. The telegraph had just been invented and was the forerunner to the telephone. It sent coded signals along electric transmission wire.

Two years later, Edison started working so that he could buy more scientific equipment. He sold candy and newspapers on the Michigan railroad. Soon he had set up a small laboratory in a baggage compartment. There he printed his own newspaper so that he could earn more money. He also learned more about telegraphy, since the train company used telegraphy to control its trains. During the American Civil War (1861–1865), Edison traveled all over the United States working as a telegrapher.

In 1868, Edison built his first invention—a device to record votes electrically. He tried to sell it to Congress, but they did not need it. After this, he made sure that he could always sell his inventions. His next invention was an improvement to the ticker machines (a telegraphic device to record and receive stock market information on paper tape). It was so successful that he was able to set up a factory to manufacture his machines. Improvements to the telegraph and typewriter soon followed.

◀ *Thomas Edison is pictured holding his electric lightbulb. Early lightbulbs did not work very well, and most people did not have access to electricity. However, Edison's lightbulb was soon lighting up the world.*

493

In 1876, Edison moved to Menlo Park, New Jersey. There he first improved the telephone. Discovering that the electrical resistance and conductivity of carbon varies according to pressure, he developed a carbon "pressure relay" to significantly amplify and improve the audibility of telephone signals. By the end of 1877, he had also developed the carbon-button transmitter, which is still used in telephone speakers and microphones.

Later that year, Edison also created his favorite invention—the phonograph. Edison wanted to find a way of recording sound. Some earlier researchers had theorized that every sound, if it could be graphically recorded, would produce a different shape, or phonograph. Edison used a spike-tipped (stylus) carbon transmitter to make impressions on a strip of waxed paper. To his amazement, the tiny indentations replayed a reproduced sound through the stylus. The phonograph made Edison world famous and was the ancestor of the record player.

Edison's other most famous invention, the lightbulb, also came from his time at Menlo Park. Edison wanted to build a safe electric light to replace gas lamps. He attempted to do this by using incandescent filaments, which produce light when heated with an electrical current. The filaments he

DID YOU KNOW?

Edison developed hearing problems during his early life. They are thought to be caused by mastoiditis, which was a condition that ran in his family. In mastoiditis, a part of the temporal bone behind the ear becomes inflamed. Edison's deafness did not appear to restrict him and it was, in fact, a strong influence on his career, providing the motivation for many of his inventions.

tried kept burning out and were of little use. After many attempts, however, he finally succeeded in 1880 by using carbonized bamboo fibers in a glass vacuum bulb. In 1882, home and offices in New York were lit by electricity for the first time.

In 1886, Edison built a large laboratory at West Orange, New Jersey, employing scientists and machine makers. It was the world's first industrial research laboratory. Edison did not excel so much in this commercial environment but remained a prolific inventor. The many inventions built there included a motion picture camera and projector. Edison died in West Orange on October 18, 1931.

▶ *Edison's remarkable phonograph made him world famous and led to the development of record players.*

See also: CARBON • CARBON FIBER • ELECTRICITY • LIGHTING • MOTION PICTURE • SOUND RECORDING • TELECOMMUNICATIONS

Einstein, Albert

> **Albert Einstein is considered by many people to be the greatest scientist of the twentieth century. He expressed his ideas mathematically—the most famous are his special and general theories of relativity. Einstein's work was particularly important in studies of the atom and astronomy.**

Albert Einstein was born in Ulm, Germany, on March 14, 1879. His family moved to Münich six weeks later, and Einstein started his schooling there at the Luitpold Gymansium. Einstein paid little attention to his studies. He often skipped classes to enjoy his favorite hobby—reading—and the only thing he seemed to enjoy was learning the violin. In later years, Einstein often attended meetings and lectures with a violin case tucked under his arm. At the age of 12, Einstein vowed to solve the riddle of the "huge world," but he went on to fail his examinations at school.

By this time Einstein's family had moved to Milan, Italy, but Einstein remained in Münich to take extra lessons in mathematics. His hard work was repaid in 1896, when he was offered a teaching fellowship in mathematics and physics at the Federal Polytechnic University in Zürich, Switzerland. Einstein graduated in 1901, lectured for a short time, and then accepted a post in the patent office in Berne, Switzerland. The same year, Einstein became a Swiss citizen.

A genius is born

During his time at the patent office, Einstein worked on a series of complex and highly original concepts in the field of theoretical physics. In 1905, he published a scientific paper entitled "On a new determination of molecular dimensions," which earned him a doctorate from Zürich University. He published four more scientific papers in 1905, any one of which would easily have earned him a doctorate. In the first paper, Einstein described electromagnetic radiation in terms of streams of particles (later called photons) to help him explain the photoelectric effect.

In the second paper, Einstein explained Brownian motion—the random motion of particles suspended in a liquid named for Scottish biologist Robert Brown (1773–1858). This phenomenon had puzzled scientists for years.

In his third paper of 1905, Einstein completely changed one of the foundations of science with his "special theory of relativity." The motion of all bodies was thought to be explained by the laws

◀ *Albert Einstein, pictured giving a lecture in 1921, completely changed the course of science without performing a single experiment. All his work stemmed from the mathematical solutions of scientific problems.*

proposed by English physicist Isaac Newton (1642–1727). Einstein showed that Newton's laws are approximately true for bodies moving at normal speeds. However, they did not explain the motion of bodies moving at or near the speed of light (186,000 miles or 300,000 kilometers per second).

In the last paper of 1905, Einstein described his equation $E=mc^2$, which shows the relationship between the energy (E) and mass (m) of a body, where c is the velocity (speed) of light.

The general theory of relativity

Einstein spent the following years teaching and developing his ideas. He worked in Berne, Zürich, and Prague, eventually becoming a professor at Berlin University in 1913. Two years later, Einstein published his general theory of relativity, which transformed ideas about gravity. He also suggested a way in which his ideas could be demonstrated practically. According to his theory, light should "bend" as it passes near a massive body such as the Sun. During an eclipse of the Sun in 1919, the light from distant stars was observed to bend as it passed the Sun—and Einstein won recognition and fame. In 1921, he was awarded the Nobel Prize for physics in recognition of his services to theoretical physics and his work on the photoelectric effect.

Campaigning for peace

Einstein was a pacifist and campaigned for this cause during World War I (1914–1918). Of Jewish descent, he was enraged by the anti-Semitism that arose in Germany during the 1920s. In 1933, German political leader Adolf Hitler (1889–1945) came to power, bringing more persecution of Jews and the added danger of war. Einstein decided to leave Germany and traveled to the United States to work at Princeton University, New Jersey.

Ironically, the pacifist Einstein had unknowingly provided the theoretical basis for the atom bomb. Also, he was persuaded to write the letter to Franklin D. Roosevelt, 32nd president of the United States, who then authorized research on the bomb. After World War II (1939–1945), Einstein campaigned strongly against any further use of the atom bomb, but he was largely ignored.

Following the publication of his general theory of relativity, Einstein tried to find a relationship between gravity and electromagnetism. He hoped to unite his ideas into one unified field theory. He published many papers but had not attained his goal when he died in his sleep on April 18, 1955.

See also: GRAVITY • RELATIVITY

Elasticity

Any substance can be made to change its size or shape if a force is applied to stretch or compress the substance. The change may be small, but it always occurs. Substances that return to their original form when a force is removed are said to be elastic.

All solids and liquids are elastic to some extent. However, the force that is applied must not exceed a certain maximum value. If a larger force is applied, the substance no longer behaves in an elastic way. It is said to have passed its "elastic limit." In solids, a process called plastic deformation causes the material to become permanently deformed. As the material no longer returns to its original form when the force is removed, the behavior is said to be inelastic.

The elastic properties of materials are important in certain branches of engineering, for example, in the design of suspension bridges and buildings. Materials that people normally think of as being quite rigid are stretched by the powerful forces present in large structures.

Hooke's law

The first person to study elasticity was English physicist Robert Hooke (1635–1703) in the late seventeenth century. He summed up his conclusions in a statement called Hooke's law. Hooke's law states that within the elastic limit of a body, the change in length that occurs is proportional to the force that causes the change.

In other words, an object being stretched is extended according to the tension applied. If a weight is hung on the end of a steel wire, for example, the wire will stretch by a certain amount. Doubling the weight will double the amount by which the wire is stretched. This will apply until the elastic limit of the wire is reached.

▲ A bungee jumper leaps off a bridge. Bungee cord is made from hundreds of strands of rubber. The elastic properties of the cord mean that the rope will stretch and absorb the energy of the falling jumper.

▲ *Rubber is made from the sap (called latex) of the rubber tree, which is cultivated in the tropics. The live trees are "tapped" to obtain the latex.*

Stress and strain

When an object, such as a wire, is stretched, a stress is applied and a strain is caused. The stress is the force applied divided by the area across the wire. The strain is the change in length produced divided by the original length of the wire. The ratio of stress divided by strain is called Young's modulus and is constant for any given material, no matter how large the stressed part. From Young's modulus, scientists can figure out how parts made from a known material will behave when a stress is applied. Young's modulus is also used for calculations on objects being compressed.

Bending objects

Different calculations are used when a force makes an object bend. Suppose, for example, that a steel rod is held upright by clamping its lower end in a vise. A horizontal force applied to the top of the rod is called a shear force. It is a force across, rather than along, the rod. The shear force makes the rod bend, so the rod changes in shape, not in size. The shear force produces a shear stress in the rod. This stress is equal to the shear force divided by the area across the rod.

The unit of shear stress is a measure of the amount by which the rod is distorted. It is equal to the distance that the top of the rod moves, divided by the original length of the rod. The amount of shear stress related to the unit shear strain is called the shear modulus (rigidity modulus) of the material. Using this figure instead of Young's modulus, Hooke's law can be applied to bending objects, too.

Another material property related to elasticity is called the bulk modulus and is used in problems where a pressure causes a change in the overall bulk (volume) of an object. The bulk modulus is the pressure (stress) divided by the proportional change in the volume.

See also: FORCES • PRESSURE • RUBBER

Electrical measurement

Various devices are used to detect, measure, and control the current running through electric circuits. Most devices make use of a deflecting force, called torque, on a current-carrying coil moving through magnetic fields. The size of deflection is proportional to the current flowing through the device.

The basic electrical meter is the galvanometer. This device measures the torque exerted on a current-carrying coil, which is pivoted between the poles of a permanent magnet. When a current passes through a wire, a magnetic field is set up around the wire. If the wire is coiled, it becomes an electromagnet whose strength depends on the strength of the current passing through it. So, as the current passes through the coil, the coil is deflected by the magnetic field. The magnitude of the deflection depends on the size of the current flowing through the coil. By standardizing the deflection to a scale, the current can be measured.

In the most sensitive galvanometers, the current-carrying coil is suspended on fine copper or gold ribbons, rather than being pivoted. These ribbons act as electrical leads to the coil as well as giving the coil its necessary return torque. The advantage of ribbons over even the best jeweled pivots or bearings is that there is less frictional resistance to the movement. As a result, galvanometers are more sensitive to small currents.

▶ *Analog (left) and digital (right) voltmeters measure the electric potential between two points in an electric circuit. Leads attached to the terminals of the voltmeters are placed at different points in the circuit. Only a very small current flows through the leads and into the voltmeters, because the voltmeters contain large resistors. The exact size of the current flowing into the voltmeters is a measure of the electric potential difference between the two points.*

Electrical current is measured in amperes, with milliamperes (one thousandth of an ampere) and microamperes (one millionth of an ampere) used for smaller currents. (These words are usually shortened to amps, milliamps, and microamps.) The maximum current a galvanometer can measure is about 50 microamps.

Ammeters

An ammeter is a galvanometer placed in parallel with a shunt, which is a conductor of very low resistance. When the ammeter is placed in an electric circuit, only a tiny, but proportional, fraction of the electrical current passes through the galvanometer, producing a deflection. There are two basic types of ammeter—the moving-coil ammeter and the moving-iron, or moving-magnet, ammeter.

Moving-coil ammeters have three basic parts: a permanent magnet, a flat coil that rests on a shaft set at right angles to the permanent magnet's field, and a coil spring. The moving coil carries the instrument's pointer. It usually pivots on bearings. The spring holds the rotation of the coil in check.

Moving-coil ammeters measure direct current up to a fixed maximum. This maximum can be as low as 25 microamps in sensitive instruments. To measure alternating currents (AC), rectifiers—devices that turn AC into direct current (DC)—must be added to the circuit.

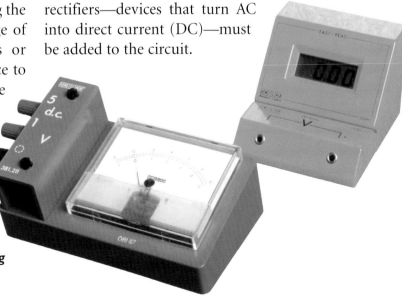

In the moving-iron ammeter, one end of the pointer is attached to a spring and the other end to a piece of soft iron. Another piece of soft iron is fixed near the first. Magnetic fields are formed when the current to be measured passes through a coil surrounding the entire movement. The iron pieces repel, and the pointer moves against its spring. With this type of ammeter, it does not matter whether the current being measured is AC or DC. Moving-iron ammeters are simple and cheap, but they are less sensitive and accurate than moving-coil ammeters and so are not used much any more.

Currents can also be measured by an electronic device that has no mechanical moving parts. This type of instrument usually acts as a voltmeter. The voltage across a resistor in the circuit can be used to indicate the current. Electronic ammeters are very accurate and have a digital display.

The voltmeter

Voltmeters register the voltage, or electric potential, between two points in an electric circuit. It is the electric potential difference that causes an electrical current to flow between the two points.

There are four main types of voltmeters: moving-coil, moving-iron, electrostatic, and digital. The first two types—moving-coil and moving-iron volt-meters—are in fact galvanometers placed in series with a large resistor. For the measurement of alternating voltages with moving-coil voltmeters, a rectifier is added to the voltmeter circuit. This ensures that DC flows through the device.

The electrostatic voltmeter gives a reading of voltage without drawing an electrical current. It uses the fact that bodies at different electrical potentials (voltages) are attracted to each other. The rotating parts of the instrument are connected to the higher potential and the fixed parts to the lower potential. The pointer is attached to the rotating parts and so registers the voltage.

The digital voltmeter uses integrated circuits to compare the voltage to be measured with its own reference voltage. The digital voltmeter is very accurate. The digital display often gives readings accurate to a few thousandths of an amp.

Potentiometers

A potentiometer is an instrument that measures or controls electrical currents. Potentiometers may be of the sliding-wire type, dividers for measuring large amounts of electricity, or the "pots" that control the tone and volume in sound amplifiers.

The potentiometer works by balancing voltage. Thus, if two batteries are connected, the electromotive force—the "driving force"—in the

▼ *Rows of electricity meters are used to measure the power generated at a plant in Florida.*

▲ Electric utility companies use watt-hour meters to measure the amount of electricity used by customers in their homes. The dials on the meter (shown above) register the customer's electricity consumption.

circuit will be the difference in the two battery voltages. This difference will cause a current to flow around the circuit, and the difference can then be measured using a galvanometer. If, however, there is no reading on the galvanometer, then there is no current and the two batteries are balanced. In other words, they have the same voltage.

The sliding-wire potentiometer

Small voltages can be measured using a sliding-wire potentiometer. To do this, galvanometer readings are taken to find the point on the sliding wire where the voltage is the same as the voltage of the battery. The distance to this point from the terminals is then measured. The procedure is then repeated, and another measurement taken, this time using a standard cell of a known voltage. From the two distance measurements and the known voltage, the unknown voltage of the battery can be determined.

The standard cell is the standard against which all potentiometer measurements are made to find unknown voltages or currents. Standard cells must provide a known voltage that does not change with time. In precise work, the voltage of the standard cell is periodically checked against a freshly made standard to ensure that it has not changed.

Voltage dividers, rheostats, and "pots"

To measure large voltages, a voltage divider is used. This device consists of a chain of resistors that can make the voltage smaller by a known fraction, so that it can then be measured in the normal way. The actual voltage can then be found by multiplying by the appropriate factor.

Another kind of potentiometer is called the rheostat. Rheostats can change the current flowing in a circuit by varying the resistance. They are often used in physics laboratories. A small version of the rheostat, called a "pot," is used in electronic equipment, such as amplifiers.

Watt-hour meter

The most common electricity meter in the home is called the watt-hour meter. Watt-hour meters measure the consumption of electricity in units called kilowatt-hours. One kilowatt-hour is 1,000 watt-hours—the amount of electricity used by ten 100-watt light bulbs in one hour.

In the watt-hour meter, a coil of thick wire carries most of the current to be measured. This coil is placed just below a horizontal aluminum disk. A shunt coil consisting of many turns of fine wire is situated above the aluminum disk. The disk rotates between the poles of a permanent magnet.

The electromagnetic fields set up by the two wire coils induce small electrical currents, called eddy currents, in the aluminum disk. The eddy currents make the disk rotate at a speed proportional to the amount of electrical power passing through the meter. A gear at the top of the disk spindle drives dials that register the amount of electricity used.

Industrial power networks often use polyphase meters. These have two driving elements (three wire) or three driving elements (four wire), each acting on a separate disk on a common spindle. The drives can also be concentrated on a single disk.

See also: ELECTRIC CIRCUIT • ELECTRICITY • MAGNETISM • RESISTOR

Electric circuit

All electrical devices, from digital wristwatches to personal computers, are powered by the movement of electrons through pathways called electric circuits. Electric circuits are designed carefully so that the devices will do what they are intended to do.

Everything in the universe consists of tiny particles called atoms. Smaller particles, called electrons, revolve around the dense nuclei at the center of atoms. Electrons carry a tiny negative electrical charge. In some materials, such as metals, some electrons can easily become separated from their atoms. If the electrons are made to flow around an electric circuit, they can be used to power electrical devices such as flashlights or radios.

A simple electric circuit

Electrons flow around an electric circuit only when it is a closed loop. In a pocket flashlight, for example, a battery drives electrons around the circuit. Electrons flow out of one end of the battery (called the negative terminal), while other electrons flow in at the opposite end (the positive terminal). Chemical reactions inside the battery "push" electrons around the circuit. This electrical "push" is called voltage. A voltage is always needed to make an electrical current flow.

The electrons from the flashlight battery flow along a metal wire. The wire runs along the flashlight case and touches the metal base of the bulb. As electrons flow into the bulb and through a coiled tungsten filament, the filament becomes very hot and glows brightly.

The electrons continue around the circuit. They flow out of the bulb into another wire that runs along the case of the flashlight and passes through a switch. When the switch is off, a gap in the wire blocks the flow of electrons. When the switch is on,

▲ *This boy is using a flashlight to read a book in bed. The flashlight contains a battery, a bulb, and a switch connected by metal conducting wires. Pushing the switch completes the circuit, and the bulb lights up.*

a piece of metal closes the gap in the circuit so that the electrons can flow without interruption. The electrons then flow from the switch along the wire and enter the battery at the positive terminal. The electrons keep flowing around the circuit unless there is a break in the circuit.

Series or parallel

In the flashlight, electrons flow through the battery, the switch, and the bulb in turn. Engineers say that these components (parts) are in series, or they form a series circuit. If any one component is removed, the circuit is broken and electrons cannot flow.

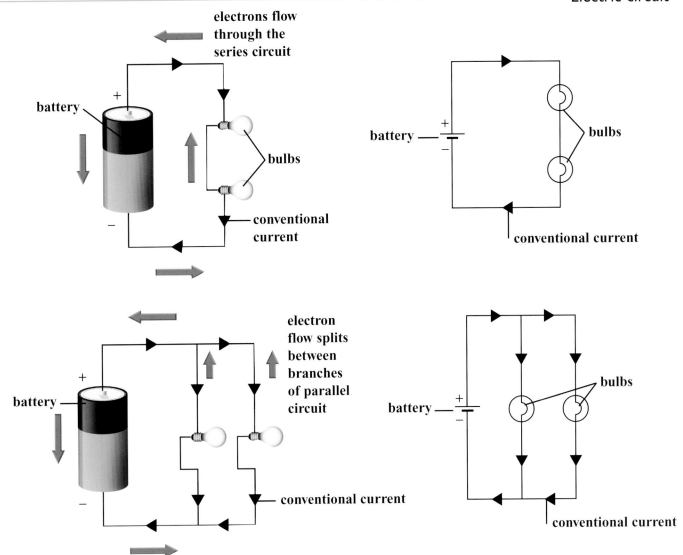

▲ *These illustrations show the electron flow through a series circuit (top) and a parallel circuit (bottom). By convention, the direction of current flow is shown from positive to negative in circuit diagrams. However, the electrons actually move from negative to positive.*

In other devices, the circuit may branch into two or more paths, which later rejoin. Each time an electron goes around the circuit, it passes along one of these paths but not all of them. If the circuit is broken in one of the branches, current continues to flow in the other branches. Engineers say that these components (parts) in the different branches are in parallel, or they form a parallel circuit.

Resistance
The amount of current that flows in a circuit depends on the voltage in the circuit and on the resistance of each component. The more resistance a component has, the less current flows. The wires connecting components have very little resistance; a bulb has much more. Circuits often include components called resistors, which have a known resistance. Circuit designers use resistors to control the amount of current flowing in the circuit.

Circuit diagrams
When engineers draw diagrams of circuits, they do not make them realistic. The actual sizes, positions, and shapes of components are not important. Engineers use standard symbols for such things as bulbs, resistors, and switches. The connecting wires are represented by a straight line.

See also: BATTERY • ELECTRICITY • ELECTRONICS • PRINTED CIRCUIT • RESISTOR • TRANSISTOR

Electricity

Electricity is the name given to various phenomena involving the movement or accumulation of charged particles. Electrical forces shape almost every aspect of the universe, from the basic structure of the atom to spectacular bolts of lightning in the sky. People did not know that electricity existed a few hundred years ago. Now most people use it every day—to heat and light their homes and to use appliances such as computers and television sets.

Everything in the world consists of tiny particles called atoms. Atoms are made up of even smaller particles: neutrons, protons, and electrons. Neutrons have no electrical charge, but the protons and electrons have charges that are equal in strength, but opposite in effect. There are an equal number of protons and electrons in most atoms, so the charges of the protons and electrons cancel out, making the atom electrically neutral. If the balance of electrons and protons in a substance is upset, however, then the object will show signs of being charged. Charged objects have the ability to attract or repel other charged objects. They may also cause sparking—lightning is simply a giant spark of electricity passing through the air.

There are two types of electrical charge. Electrons carry a tiny negative charge, and protons carry an equal, but opposite, positive charge. A negatively charged object has more electrons than protons. Conversely, a positively charged object has more protons than electrons.

Charging by friction
A plastic pen can be charged simply by rubbing it with a woolen cloth. This is an example of charging by friction. Electrons are "rubbed off" the atoms

▲ Lightning is a powerful electrical discharge in the sky. It follows a process called charge separation, which takes place in cumulonimbus clouds. Negative charges migrate toward the base of the cloud. This induces a positive charge near the ground. When the charge imbalance between the clouds and the ground becomes large enough, lightning strikes.

that make up the plastic pen and become attached to the atoms of the woolen cloth. As a result, the pen, which is left with more protons than electrons, will have a positive charge. The cloth, now with an excess of electrons, will have a negative charge.

Charged objects

Two objects with opposite electrical charges attract one another. So the cloth used to charge the pen will be attracted by the pen. However, objects with the same kind of charge repel, or push each other away. If two balloons are charged in the same way as the plastic pen and then brought close together, the balloons will tend to push each other apart.

One thing that all charged objects have in common is that they tend to attract light, uncharged objects. When someone cleans the surface of a compact disc, for example, friction charges the disc and it will attract dust. The same force of attraction causes an uncharged piece of paper to fly up and stick to a positively charged plastic pen (see the illustration below).

Under the right conditions, a charged object will retain its charge forever. Since the electricity stays where it is, it is called static electricity. The study of electricity in this state is called electrostatics.

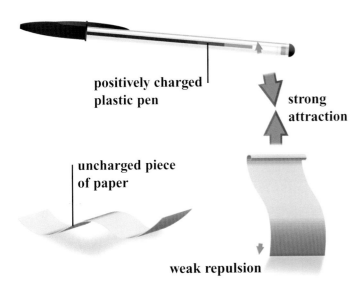

positively charged plastic pen

strong attraction

uncharged piece of paper

weak repulsion

▲ *A plastic pen and a piece of paper can be used to illustrate electrostatic induction. Rubbing a pen with a woolen cloth gives the pen a positive charge. When the pen is held over the paper, electrons are attracted through the paper toward the pen. The pen induces (causes) a charge separation in the paper. It makes one part of the paper negatively charged and the other part positively charged. The positively charged pen then attracts the negatively charged part of the paper, and the paper flies up and sticks to the pen.*

Electrostatic machines

It could be said that modern research into electricity started in 1600 with English amateur scientist William Gilbert (1544–1603), who was also court physician to Queen Elizabeth I (1533–1603). Gilbert found that when he rubbed certain objects, such as amber, glass, and sulfur, with a cloth, they would attract light objects. He called these objects "electrics," after the Greek word *elektron*, which means "amber."

The first electrostatic generator was built sixty years later by German scientist Otto von Guericke (1602–1686), who was mayor of Magdeburg in present-day Germany. Von Guericke's machine consisted of a small sulfur ball that was rubbed by hand as it was rotated by a crank. Von Guericke clearly saw the static electricity, but he did not use the machine to conduct electrical experiments.

About 1676, French astronomer Jean Picard (1620–1682) noted that a glow appeared above the mercury in his barometers when he moved them around his laboratory in the dark. Picard found that the glow was strongest when the mercury was moving up and down in the tube. In 1703, English instrument maker and self-taught scientist Francis Hauksbee (died c. 1713) heard about Picard's glowing mercury barometers. Hauksbee lived during a time when lighting involved fire, candles, and oil lamps. He realized that Picard's new light source could be very useful, so he set about trying to recreate the glow. Three years later, Hauksbee succeeded by rubbing a turning glass globe with the palm of his hand.

By the end of the eighteenth century, a number of German scientists had experimented with electrostatic machines. Their favorite type consisted of a glass globe rubbed by a leather or silk pad. The electrical charge was produced by friction as the pad rubbed against the glass. The charge was then collected by means of an insulated metal tube with pointed ends, called the prime conductor. This tube was held in place close to the surface of the rotating glass. The electrical charge produced was often high enough to give a severe shock or to cause a spectacular spark.

Franklin's experiments

The famous electrical experiments of U.S. statesman and amateur scientist Benjamin Franklin (1706–1790) were based on those of English minister and scientist Joseph Priestley (1733–1804). In 1769, Franklin built an electrostatic generator based on a design by Priestley. Franklin used the machine to study the effects of static electricity. Looking up to the sky on a stormy night, he wondered whether lightning was caused by electricity, too. He decided to try collecting electricity from the clouds.

Franklin fixed a metal rod to a kite, which he flew during a thunderstorm. Electricity picked up by the metal rod passed down the damp kite string to a large metal key tied to the lower end. Franklin held a piece of silk ribbon that was tied to the key. Silk is an insulator—a substance that does not allow electricity to pass through it—so the charge on the key could not escape. Then, Franklin touched the key. Sparks flew, and he felt a powerful shock through his body. This proved, beyond doubt, that the clouds were charged with electricity.

Electrical currents

Franklin and other early experimenters used a form of capacitor to store electrical charge. The capacitor was a simple device that consisted of two metal plates separated by an insulating material, such as glass. When the two plates were connected by a wire, a spark was produced. It was caused by a burst of electrons flowing through the wire from the negative plate to the positive plate. This flow of electrons is called an electrical current.

For some time, little progress was made in understanding electricity. The problem was that a capacitor soon lost its charge, so the current it provided quickly died away. A reliable source of steady electrical current was finally discovered in the late eighteenth century, and this discovery came about quite by chance.

In 1771, Luigi Galvani (1737–1798), Italian physician and professor of anatomy at Bologna University, was dissecting frogs in the laboratory. When Galvani hung the frogs from a brass hook on an iron rail, he noticed that the dead frogs' legs

◀ *This picture shows a boy touching a machine called a Van de Graaf generator and at the same time holding his brother's hand. The Van de Graaf generator is an electrical machine that produces extremely high voltage at low, safe levels of electrical current. When the boy touches the metal ball at the top of the generator, electrical charge passes through him and his brother and passes out of their bodies. As the electrical charge flows through the boys' hair, each hair is charged to the same voltage. The hairs repel each other, which makes the hair stand on end.*

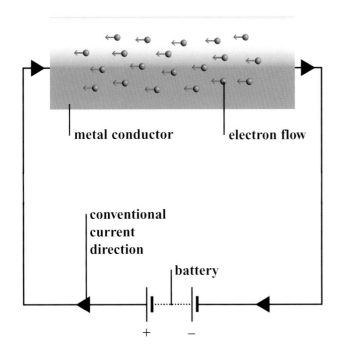

metal conductor   electron flow

conventional
current
direction

battery

+   −

▲ *When electrical engineers draw circuit diagrams, they show the direction of current from positive to negative. In fact, the electrons move through a circuit from the negative terminal of the battery, along the wire, to the positive terminal. The positive-negative convention reflects Benjamin Franklin's original designation of positive and negative current flow.*

pile, one on top of the other, separating each pair with cardboard soaked in salt water. When Volta touched the two ends of the pile, he felt a shock. Volta continued to add to the pile and found that the higher the pile, the stronger the electric shock. With a very high pile of silver and zinc disks, Volta could heat fine wires until they glowed. Volta had, in fact, constructed the first battery. He announced his invention, called the "voltaic pile," to the Royal Society, London, in March 1800.

An electrical revolution

Volta's battery was a very important invention. For this first time, scientists had a reliable source of electricity to use for their research, and many important discoveries soon followed.

One such discovery was made by English chemists Anthony Carlisle (1768–1840) and William Nicholson (1753–1815). Using a battery, Carlisle and Nicholson passed an electrical current through salt water and found that hydrogen gas was released. They had discovered a process called electrolysis—using electricity to break down compounds into the elements from which they are made. Soon after this experiment, English scientist Humphry Davy (1778–1829) used electrolysis to isolate the elements potassium and sodium.

Electromagnetism

In 1819, Danish physicist Hans Christian Ørsted (1777–1851) made another important discovery. Ørsted was demonstrating the heating effect of an electrical current in a lecture to his students. During the experiment, Ørsted noticed that a nearby compass needle changed from its normal north-south direction whenever he turned the current on. Ørsted had discovered electromagnetism. When the wire carried a current, it acted like a magnet, and the compass needle moved.

Ørsted's discovery fueled an enormous amount of research into electromagnetism. A few years later, French scientist André-Marie Ampère (1775–1836) demonstrated that two wires carrying current in the same direction attracted one another, while two wires carrying current in opposite

witched. Galvani realized that electricity was causing the legs to twitch, but he did not know where the electricity came from. He decided that the twitching was caused by the muscles and nerves in the frogs' legs. He announced that he had discovered "animal electricity."

Italian physicist Alessandro Volta (1745–1827) was intrigued by Galvani's work. Volta repeated the experiment using different metals and animals and also tried out the experiment on himself. He placed two different metals on his tongue and experienced an unpleasant sensation on his tongue. Volta realized that Galvani's "animal electricity" was conventional electrical current produced between different metals—the brass hook and the iron railing. The twitch of the frogs' legs had been a response to the electricity in the metals, not the cause of it.

To prove his point, Volta constructed the first practical electric cell and battery. He gathered pairs of silver and zinc disks and piled them up in a huge

Electromagnetic induction

In 1821, English scientist Michael Faraday (1791–1867) used electricity to produce continuous motion when he invented the first electric motor. Ten years later, he discovered how magnetism could be used to generate electricity. Faraday noticed that moving a magnet near a wire coil produced an electrical current in the wire. The electrical current produced by a changing magnetic field is called an induced current. Faraday used induced currents to build the first electricity generator. Generators are now used in power stations to supply homes and factories with electricity.

Four simple equations

In 1864, Scottish physicist James Clerk Maxwell (1831–1879) combined the work of Ørsted, Ampère, Faraday, and others into four simple equations, known as Maxwell's equations, which describe completely the sources and interactions of electrical and magnetic fields. Maxwell's equations

▲ *Brightly colored neon lights illuminate a street in Las Vegas. Much of the city's electricity supply comes from generators at the nearby Hoover Dam. The Hoover Dam produces enough power each year to light up 1.7 million homes.*

▶ *This engraving of André-Marie Ampère was made by French artist Ambroise Tardieu (1788–1841) in 1825. In recognition of Ampère's contribution to the study of electricity, electrical current is measured in units called amperes (amps for short).*

directions repelled each other. From his experiments, Ampère devised a simple law, called Ampère's law, to calculate the size of magnetic force due to a current-carrying wire. With his colleague, French scientist François Arago (1786–1853), Ampère also demonstrated that a current-carrying wire twisted in the shape of a coil produced a magnetic field similar to that of a bar magnet. By increasing the current flowing through the coil, Ampère and Arago found that the strength of the magnet increased. They called the coil a solenoid, after the Greek word *solen,* meaning "pipe."

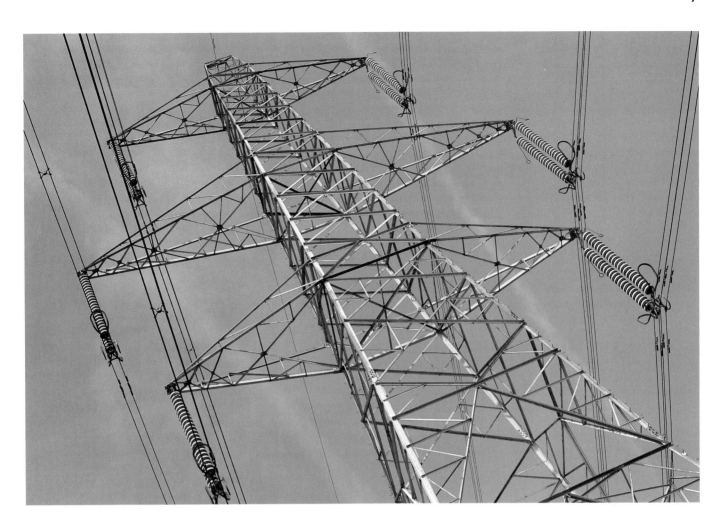

▲ *Overhead power lines carry high-voltage electrical current from power stations to consumers across a vast, interconnected power transmission system, called a grid. For reasons of safety and aesthetics, overhead lines are usually used in rural areas. In urban centers, underground power lines are more common.*

also predicted the existence of electromagnetic radiation, which was unheard of at the time but was later discovered by German physicist Heinrich Hertz (1857–1894) in 1887.

Electricity at work

The world's first central electrical power plant was built by U.S. inventor Thomas Alva Edison (1847–1931). Edison's power plant was built on Pearl Street in downtown New York City, and it opened in 1882. The generator was able to supply electricity to 2,323 lamps at one time, the number in use the first day of operation. By 1884, the Pearl Street plant lit 11,272 lamps in five hundred different buildings. In addition, Edison provided single generators to supply lighting for nearly 60,000 more lamps. By 1885, there were a quarter of a million electric lights in use in the United States. Similar growth occurred in other countries.

Electricity is now generated for use in homes, offices, street lighting, and public buildings such as railroad stations. Most electricity is generated by burning fossil fuels, such as coal, natural gas, and oil. However, hydroelectric power plants, which use water to turn huge turbine blades, provide around 10 percent of the total amount of electricity used by consumers in the United States. Other sources of electric power include nuclear fission, solar cells, tides, and the wind.

See also: BATTERY • CAPACITOR • COMPASS • ELECTRIC CIRCUIT • ELECTRIC MOTOR • ELECTROMAGNETISM • MAGNETISM

Glossary

Absolute zero The lowest possible theoretical temperature limit, measured on the Kelvin scale as 0K (−459.67°F or −273.15°C).

Atom The smallest particle of an element that can exist on its own in nature.

Atmosphere The layer of gaseous chemicals surrounding Earth. The atmosphere provides oxygen and contains water vapor, which falls as precipitation. It also protects Earth from radiation and meteors.

Biome Any of Earth's major ecosystems that extend over large areas and are characterized by a distinctive climate and vegetation.

Carcinogen Any substance or agent that causes a normal cell to become cancerous.

Chromosome A threadlike strand of coiled deoxyribonucleic acid (DNA) composed of genes.

Condensation A change of physical state from a gas to a liquid, or from a liquid to a solid.

Corona Outermost layer of the Sun's atmosphere that becomes visible only during total solar eclipses.

Digital Relating to or using calculation by numerical methods. Especially for use by a computer.

Ecosystem An interdependent community of living organisms functioning together within its nonliving environment as a unit.

Equator The imaginary circle around Earth's surface equidistant from the poles. It divides Earth into the Northern Hemisphere and the Southern Hemisphere.

Fault Fracture in rock along which the rocks on either side have been displaced relative to one another.

Gene A hereditary unit consisting of a segment of DNA. Each gene occupies a specific location on a chromosome and determines a particular characteristic in an organism.

Hydroelectricity The electricity generated when using water to drive a turbine.

Mordants Chemicals (such as tannic acid combined with various metal salts or, sometimes, the salts alone) used to fix dyes in or on a substance by combining with the dye to form an insoluble compound.

Pangaea Supercontinent in Earth's history formed of the landmasses Gondwana and Laurasia.

Pathogen Any agent that provokes an immune response from an organism. Bacteria are pathogens.

Peristalsis The contractions of muscle that occur in the walls of hollow organs, such as parts of the digestive system, that move the contents of the organ through the tube.

Piezoelectricity The electricity emitted by certain crystals when placed under mechanical pressure.

Placebo In pharmacology, an inert or innocuous substance used as a control in experiment testing the effectiveness of an active substance (such as a drug).

Plasma One of the four states of matter, plasma is a collection of charged particles in which the numbers of positive and negative ions are approximately equal.

Precipitation Hail, rain, sleet, or snow that condenses in the atmosphere and falls to Earth's surface.

Radioactivity The spontaneous disintegration of unstable nuclei, which is accompanied by the emission of particles or rays.

Rectifier In electronics, a device used for converting alternating current (AC) into direct current (DC).

Ribosomes Structures within cells that are the sites of protein synthesis.

Solenoid A round coil of wire that behaves like a bar magnet when electrical current passes through it.

Strain Deformation or change of volume of a body or part of a body due to an applied stress.

Stress System of forces in equilibrium applied to deform a body.

Torque Force that tends to produce rotation.

Transcription The production of a molecule of ribonucleic acid (RNA) from a DNA template.

Translation Ribosomal stage of protein synthesis when information provided by messenger RNA (mRNA) is translated into a particular sequence of amino acids in a polypeptide chain.

Vaporization A change of physical state from a liquid to a gas.

Index

Page numbers in **bold** refer to main articles; those in *italics* refer to illustrations.